Independent Schools
Examinations Board

MATHEMATICS

ISEB Revision Guide
(Second edition)

Stephen Froggatt

Edited by David Hanson

Published by ISEB Publications, an imprint of Galore Park Publishing Ltd
19/21 Sayers Lane, Tenterden, Kent TN30 6BW

www.galorepark.co.uk

Text copyright © Stephen Froggat 2007

The right of Stephen Froggatt to be identified as the author of this Work has been
asserted by him in accordance with sections 77 and 78 of the Copyright, Designs and
Patents Act 1988.

Design and typography Stephen Austin & Sons Ltd., Hertford.

Printed by Replika Press, India

ISBN-13: 978 0 903627 45 0

First edition published 1999
Second edition published 2007, reprinted 2007

Details of other ISEB Revision Guides for Common Entrance, examination papers and
Galore Park publications are available at www.galorepark.co.uk

ACKNOWLEDGEMENTS

I owe many thanks to all my own teachers, especially David Bunce and John Knee; all of whom helped to shape the idea that 'Maths Is Fun' while I was still learning myself. While teaching, I have been inspired by many colleagues in the Maths Departments of Seven Kings High School, Highfield Preparatory School and Oaks Park High School, in particular my first Head of Department, Margaret Quinney – thank you, all of you, for the tips, the puzzles and the enthusiasm – and for the infectious love of teaching Maths! Thank you too to all those fellow delegates at all those wonderful Maths Conferences over the years, for the fun and friendship, and for teaching me that I have so much still to learn: the list is long, but special thanks to Michael Ede, Andrew Jeffrey, Martin Elston, Moira Laffey and to all those others at the IAPS, SATIPS and Charterhouse sessions who continue to inspire by their excellent example, and whose vast treasury of magical ideas I have so shamelessly plundered ever since.

For this edition I extend particular thanks once again to my editor David Hanson, former Aberlour House Deputy Head, for the helpful advice about this new structure, the long hours of cross-checking, the brilliant illustrations in the dictionary and the endless supplies of strong coffee and chocolate biscuits.

Finally, sincere thanks to all my pupils, past and present, who have helped shape my own understanding of why 'Maths Is Fun And I Like It', and who provide each day the reason I have the best job in the world. To them and future pupils this book is dedicated.

THE AUTHOR

Stephen Froggatt B.Sc., P.G.C.E. is currently Team Leader for Mathematics at Oaks Park High School, Ilford. Previously he was Head of Maths at Highfield Preparatory School, Liphook. In his spare time he maintains the website www.MathsIsFun.net because it is.

A NOTE CONCERNING THE LAYOUT OF MATERIAL IN THIS BOOK

1. *To avoid unnecessary repetition, sometimes a topic in the 11+ section may be covered in greater depth than is required by the 11+ paper.*
2. *Similarly, in the 13+ section, the syllabus and copies of past papers will be needed to determine the level of difficulty of questions in the two levels of papers. This is particularly important in Number and Algebra.*
3. *It must be remembered that candidates should be familiar with the topics in all strands up to Level 4 of the National Curriculum.*

CONTENTS

NOTE TO PUPILS ix

11+ NUMBER AND ALGEBRA TOPICS

Multiplication and Division by 10 and 100 (whole numbers only) 1

Mental Arithmetic Strategies 2

Addition and Subtraction of Decimals to 2 Decimal Places 3

'Short' Multiplication and Division (by a single digit number) 4

The Fraction Wall: Fractions and Percentage Equivalents 5

Exploring and Describing Number Patterns 6

Types of Number: Multiple, Factor, Prime and Square 7

Word Formulae and Function Machines 8

First Quadrant Co-ordinates 9

Negative Numbers in Context 10

11+ SHAPE AND SPACE TOPICS

Drawing Solids and Nets 11

Triangle Construction using Ruler, Compasses and Protractor 12

Symmetry and Congruence 13

Reflection in a Diagonal (sloping) Line 14

Reading Scales 15

The Metric System 16

Metric and Imperial Units 17

Perimeter, Area and Volume 18

Directions with the Eight-Point Compass 19

3 Transformations: Reflection, Rotation and Translation 20

11+ HANDLING DATA TOPICS

Frequency Tables Using Discrete Data 21

Finding The Mode, Median and Range 22

Calculating the Mean 23

Comparing Distributions 23

Grouped Data and Equal Class Intervals 24

Line Graphs and Conversion Graphs 25

Words to Describe Probability 26

13+ NUMBER AND ALGEBRA TOPICS

Multiplying and Dividing by 10, 100 and 1000 (including decimals) 27

Multiplication and Division of Decimals to 2 Decimal Places 28

Addition and Subtraction with Negative Numbers 29

Multiplication and Division with Negative Numbers 30

Prime Factorisation (products of powers of primes) 31

Calculating **A** as a Fraction of **B** 32

Calculating a Fraction or Percentage of a Quantity 33

Calculating with Ratios 34

Ordering and Rounding Decimals 35

Introduction to Pencil and Paper Multiplication and Division 36

Long Multiplication (standard or 'compact' method) 37

Long Multiplication (alternative methods) 38

Inverses and Approximations as Checks 39

Using one Calculation to find the Answer to Another 40

BODMAS and Algebraic Substitution 41

Simple Symbolic Formulae 42

Four-Quadrant Co-ordinates and Graphical Mappings 43

Fraction, Decimal and Percentage Equivalents 44

Addition, Subtraction, Multiplication and Division of Fractions 45

Describing Sequences in Words 46

n^{th} Term: Describing the nth Term of a Sequence in Words 47

Solving Simple Linear Equations 48

Forming and Solving Linear Equations 49

Significant Figures 50

Estimation 51

Interpreting Calculator Displays 51

Calculating Fractions and Percentages with a Calculator 52

13+ SHAPE AND SPACE TOPICS

Angle Laws for Straight Lines and Polygons 53

Reflection Symmetry in Plane Shapes 54

Rotation Symmetry in Plane Shapes 55

Isometric Drawing of 3-Dimensional Objects 56

Quadrilaterals 57

Circles: Circumference, Area and Circular Volume Calculations 58

Enlargement: Centre of Enlargement and Scale Factor 59

Enlargement: Area Factor 60

Fractional and Composite Areas 61

Three-Figure Bearings and Scale Drawing 62

13+ HANDLING DATA TOPICS

Drawing Conclusions from Graphs, Charts and Diagrams 63

Frequency Diagrams (bar charts) using Discrete Data.. 64

Pie Charts 65

Theoretical and Experimental Probability 66

Probability Calculations 67

Listing Outcomes Systematically 68

Scattergraphs and Correlation 69

Sets and Venn Diagrams 70

13+ (EXTENDED SYLLABUS) NUMBER AND ALGEBRA TOPICS

Quadratic Equations by Trial and Improvement 71

n^{th} Term: Describing the nth Term of a Sequence Algebraically 72

n^{th} Term: Quadratic Sequences 73

Simultaneous Equations (algebraic and graphical solution methods) 74

Solving Inequalities and Finding Integer Solution Sets 75

13+ (EXTENDED SYLLABUS) SHAPE AND SPACE TOPICS

Pythagoras' Theorem 76

Fractional and Composite Volumes 77

Distance, Speed and Time Calculations 78

Trigonometry 79

Personal Notes Page 80

11+ REFERENCE SECTION

Multiplication Tables 81

Prime Numbers 81

Squares, Cubes and Roots 82

The 24-hour Clock 83

The Number Line 83

Odd and Even Numbers and Rules 84

Types of Triangle 85

Types of Quadrilateral 85

Metric and Imperial Unit Conversions 86

Types of Angle 87

The Compass Points 87

Quadrilateral Classification 88

Venn and Carroll Diagrams 88

13+ REFERENCE SECTION

Triangular Numbers 89

Names of the Polygons 90

Angles in Regular Polygons 90

Area and Volume Formulae 91

Parts of the Circle 92

The Value of Pi 92

Sets and Venn Diagrams 93

13+ (EXTENDED SYLLABUS) REFERENCE SECTION

Algebraic and Pythagorean Formulae 94

GENERAL REFERENCE SECTION

Revision Guidelines 95

Examination Guidelines 96

Glossary (dictionary) and Index 97

NOTE TO PUPILS

Hello! And welcome to **your** Maths Revision book. It is not a textbook, but is designed to help you as you revise. Feel free to write in it, use colours and highlighter pens, and generally make it yours. For example, you might cross out all the Extended Syllabus 13+ Topics if you are doing Common Entrance Papers 1 and 3 – but check with your teacher first!

Why not tick off the topics you know? That way you can see how quickly you are revising. Nobody knows nothing, despite what they say, and it can be very encouraging to see your knowledge grow 'weekly' rather than 'weakly'. There is space at the back for your own extra notes or tips from your maths teacher.

Examinations are not designed to trip you up (honest!) but to give you a chance to demonstrate what you know and what you can do. Make sure that you have the facts at your fingertips so that you can show yourself off at your best.

My department motto has always been:

MATHS IS FUN AND I LIKE IT!

Why don't you adopt it?

All the very best for your examinations,

SDTF

Mathematics: A Revision Guide

ABOUT THIS BOOK

This book is organised into seven main sections:

- 11+ Topic Notes and KS2 revision
- 13+ Topic Notes (CE Papers 1 to 4 and standard KS3)
- 13+ (Extended Syllabus) Topic Notes (Papers 2, 4, Scholarship and higher KS3)
- Reference Section 11+ and KS2 Revision
- Reference Section 13+ and KS3
- Revision Techniques and Preparation for Examinations
- Glossary (dictionary) and Index

The emphasis throughout is on reminding rather than teaching, so examples have been kept to a minimum.

TENS AND HUNDREDS

> ● You need to be able to multiply and divide whole numbers by 10 or 100 without a calculator.

MULTIPLYING BY 10 OR 100

Multiplying by 10 or 100 is easy. It can be thought of as

- writing zeros at the end of the *whole* numbers
- moving digits to the left so they have a higher place value
- moving the decimal point to the right.

Examples

H T U		H T U		H T U
2 3	×	1 0	=	2 3 0
1 7 4	×	1 0 0	=	1 7 4 0 0

DIVIDING BY 10 OR 100

Dividing by 10 or 100 can be thought of as

- removing zeros from the end
- moving the figures to the right
- moving the decimal point to the left.

(Remember that whole numbers have a decimal point too – it's after the units digit!)

Examples

H T U . t h		H T U		H T U . t h	
2 1 0	÷	1 0	=	2 1	(the same as 21.0)
1 7 4	÷	1 0	=	1 7 . 4	
3 4 2 0	÷	1 0 0	=	3 4 . 2	
7	÷	1 0 0	=	0 . 0 7	and so on

To help you learn, you can play a fun game with your calculator!

Type in a number and then decide between ☒ and ☒

and then between 10 and 100

Have a guess at the answer and then press ☐ =

Were you right?

MATHSFACT
The only reason we count in tens is because of our ten fingers and toes.
A number system based on any other number would be just as easy to use.

11+

- For mental arithmetic tests, you need to have a range of strategies for speeding up calculations in your head.

CHANGE THE QUESTION!

When working out 7 × £2.99 it is much easier to change it to 7 × £3 and then subtract those seven extra pennies at the end to get £20.93

SUBTRACTION AND ADDITION IN STAGES

If you want to subtract something awkward like 54, then it is usually easier to subtract in two or more stages: first subtract the 50, then subtract the 4

Adding in stages is surprisingly similar . . .

SUBTRACTION AND ADDITION IN PARTNERSHIP

It is often a really good idea to use a combination of adding and subtracting to make the calculation easier. For example, when subtracting 17, it is probably easier to subtract 20 then add on 3 to the result.

THE FAMOUS FIVE

Multiplying by five is equivalent to multiplying by ten and then halving the answer. Dividing by five is equivalent to dividing by ten and doubling the answer. You need to try this out to see just how quick this is!

10 − 1 = 9

OK, so you knew that (I hope!) but it does give us a very handy way of multiplying by 9: just multiply by 10 then subtract the original number.

10 + 1 = 11

You can probably see where this is going . . .

To multiply by 11, just multiply by 10 then add the original number.

LAST DIGIT DELIGHTS

N/A

The last digit in any product is the product of the last digits in the two numbers being multiplied. So, for example, we know that 24 × 312 must end in an 8 since 8 is the result of 4 × 2 in the original question.

PLAYING ROUGH

Always get a rough answer before you work anything out to give you a quick check that you haven't messed it up completely. Not that YOU would, of course . . .

MATHSFACT

The number 1 is not counted as prime because it does not have two distinct factors. However, 2 is prime; it has been called 'the oddest prime of all'.

Why? Because it is the only one which is even!!

● You need to be able to add and subtract decimals to two places without a calculator.

There is really only one thing to remember on this page:

> **LINE UP THE DECIMAL POINTS!!**
> (or if you prefer, **LINE UP THE UNITS DIGITS!**)

ADDITION

Let's try adding three numbers together, bearing this rule in mind:

U.t		U.th		U.th
2.1	+	0.21	+	2.12

$$
\begin{array}{r}
\text{U.th} \\
2.1 \\
0.21 \\
+\ 2.12 \\
\hline
4.43 \\
\end{array}
$$

Correct!

SUBTRACTION

This is very similar – just make sure that you line up those decimal points. Remember also that writing zeros at the end of a decimal does not change the number, and that putting .0 or .00 on the end of a whole number is OK too. The rest, as they say . . .

$4.78 - 3.6$	$7.1 - 4.68$	$7 - 0.37$

$$
\begin{array}{r}
4.78 \\
-\ 3.60 \\
\hline
1.18 \\
\end{array}
\qquad
\begin{array}{r}
7.10 \\
-\ 4.68 \\
\hline
2.42 \\
\end{array}
\qquad
\begin{array}{r}
7.00 \\
-\ 0.37 \\
\hline
6.63 \\
\end{array}
$$

(just like doing 478 − 360) | (just like doing 710 − 468) | (same idea as 700 − 37)

MATHSFACT

The obscure Italian mathematician Francesco Pellos has the honour of being the author of the earliest-known decimal point in print. As he dotted the page, Columbus was discovering America – the year was 1492.

● The first thing to do after you have learned your tables is to learn to multiply or divide any large number by a single-digit number.

Short multiplication – multiplying by a single-digit number [e.g. 126 × 7]
The two favourite methods are the compact and partitioning methods:

compact	partitioning
126 7 **882** 1 4	$100 \times 7 = 700$ $20 \times 7 = 140$ $6 \times 7 = 42$ **882**

simple short division	division with remainder as a decimal
$384 \div 6 = 64$ 064 6 $\overline{3\,8\,4}$	$384 \div 5 = 76.8$ 076.8 5 $\overline{3\,8\,4.0}$
The zero above the three is important because it acts as a place holder and stops us getting a crazy answer such as 640 or 604 ! Always a good idea to write it in.	As before, we must write the zero above the three. We also write in **two** decimal points, one above the other, so that we can continue the division beyond it.

check by multiplying	division with remainder as a fraction
64 6 **384** 3 2	$384 \div 7 = 54\frac{6}{7}$ 054 rem. 6 7 $\overline{3\,8\,4}$
Obviously this should take us back to our original number. Hooray! It does!	Since we were dividing by 7, the remainder is put over 7 to make the fraction.

MATHSFACT
The number 4 is very special. It is a square number, the first composite number, and is equal to both 2 + 2 and 2 × 2. Only four colours are required to colour distinctly any map or pattern drawn on paper. *Four* has four letters!

N/A

FRACTIONS AND PERCENTAGES

● You need to understand the approximate sizes of the most common fractions and their percentage equivalents.

A good way to see how fractions and percentages compare is by using the 'Fraction Wall':

whole	1 (100%)								
halves	$\frac{1}{2}$				50%				
thirds	$\frac{1}{3}$		$\frac{1}{3}$		33⅓%				
quarters	$\frac{1}{4}$		$\frac{1}{4}$		25%		25%		
fifths	$\frac{1}{5}$	$\frac{1}{5}$		20%		20%		20%	
sixths	$\frac{1}{6}$	$\frac{1}{6}$	$\frac{1}{6}$	16⅔%		16⅔%		16⅔%	
eighths	$\frac{1}{8}$	$\frac{1}{8}$	$\frac{1}{8}$	$\frac{1}{8}$	12.5%	12.5%	12.5%	12.5%	
tenths	$\frac{1}{10}$ $\frac{1}{10}$ $\frac{1}{10}$ $\frac{1}{10}$ $\frac{1}{10}$					10%	10%	10%	10% 10%

Using a ruler held vertically, it is now easy to see that (for example):

$\frac{2}{6} = \frac{1}{3}$, or $\frac{8}{10} > \frac{3}{4}$

MATHSFACT
The word *fraction* comes from the Latin *frangere* (to break). A fraction is therefore simply a *broken number*.

NUMBER PATTERNS

● You need to be able to spot, explore and describe patterns in a series of numbers.

Look at these arrangements made with match sticks:

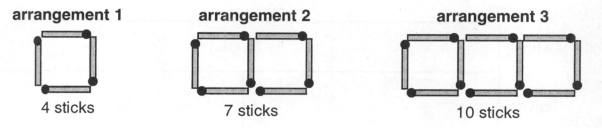

arrangement 1

4 sticks

arrangement 2

7 sticks

arrangement 3

10 sticks

Can you see a pattern here?
How many sticks are there in arrangement 4 and arrangement 5?

One of the best ways to explore number patterns is to look at the difference between each number and the next, as in this diagram:

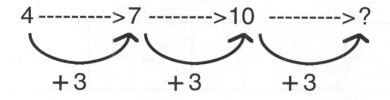

4 --------->7 --------->10 --------->?

+3   +3   +3

We can then say: 'It's going up in threes' and predict that the next number will be 13

Let's see if we were right.

arrangement 4

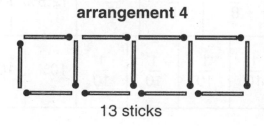

13 sticks

N/A

Oh! You're just so clever!

Now, can you predict the number of sticks needed for arrangement 10?

Arrangement 10 has 31 sticks

MATHSFACT
The number 6 is *perfect*, meaning that it is equal to the sum of all its factors except itself: the factors of 6 are 1, 2, 3 and 6; 6 = 1 + 2 + 3
The next two examples are 28 and 496. Perfect numbers are rare!

MULTIPLE, FACTOR, PRIME AND SQUARE

> ● You should be familiar with some of the more common words used to describe numbers and their properties.

For this section it really helps if you know your tables well! Let's see why they are so important.

MULTIPLES

Multiples of 3 include 3, 6, 9, 12, 15, 18, ...
Multiples of 6 include 6, 12, 18, 24, 30, 36, ...
Think of multiples as the **results** in the times table of a number.

FACTORS

Factors of 30 are all the numbers which divide exactly into 30
We can make a factor rainbow.

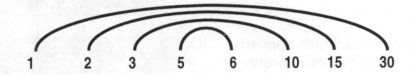

1   2   3   5   6   10   15   30

Notice how they come in pairs.

$$30 = 1 \times 30 \qquad \text{or } 2 \times 15 \qquad \text{or } 3 \times 10 \qquad \text{or } 5 \times 6$$

Think of factors as the **questions** from the times table.

PRIMES

(For a list of primes see reference page 81.)

Quite simply, a prime is a number which has only two factors: 1 and itself.

SQUARES

Any number multiplied by itself gives a **square**. In the factor rainbow this number joins to itself in the middle. *(See page 82.)* Let's try this for the number 36

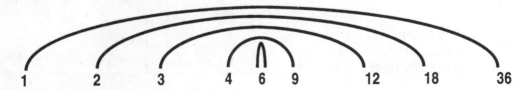

1   2   3   4   6   9   12   18   36

Notice how the 6 is joined to itself because 36 = 6 × 6

> **MATHSFACT**
> Win $100 000 by solving a maths puzzle! This prize money is available to the finder of the first 10 million-digit prime number. You could do this on your computer by downloading the free GIMPS software from www.mersenne.org

WORD FORMULAE AND FUNCTION MACHINES

- You need to be able to form and use simple formulae expressed in words or as a picture.

How many months old are you?

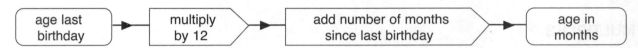

Could you follow that? I'm sure you could. It's an example of a word formula, in this case to change years and months into just months.

A word formula is a set of instructions telling you how to change one number into another.

Here's another type of word formula, written as a puzzle:

> I think of a number, double it, add 11
> and the answer is 99
> What was my number?

And now a word formula which converts degrees Celsius into degrees Fahrenheit:

> multiply by 9, divide by 5, then add 32

What are these temperatures in Fahrenheit: (a) 0 °C   (b) 40 °C   (c) 100 °C?

Two diagrams to finish:

1. Function machine

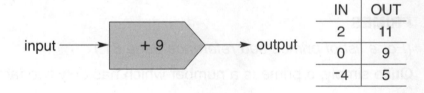

IN	OUT
2	11
0	9
-4	5

2. Flow chart

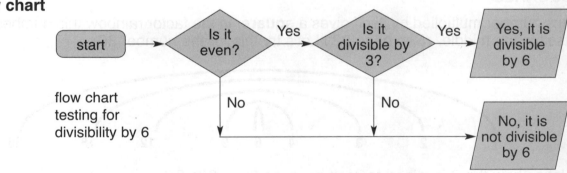

flow chart testing for divisibility by 6

(a) 32 °F   (b) 104 °F   (c) 212 °F

My number was 44

MATHSFACT

8 is the smallest number of small cubes needed to build a larger cube (2 × 2 × 2).

11+

● You should be able to read and plot co-ordinates using positive whole numbers.

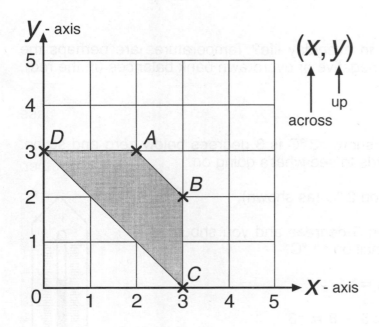

(x, y)

up

across

In the beginning...

The point (0, 0) is the reference point for all co-ordinates. It is called the *origin*.

The point A is at (2, 3): 2 across, 3 up

The point B is at (3, 2): 3 across, 2 up

The point C is at (3, 0): 3 across, 0 up   (It stays on the *x* axis.)

The point D is at (0, 3): 0 across, 3 up   (It stays on the *y* axis.)

If we were to slide the shape across or up (or both), we could redraw it anywhere else on the grid. This sliding move is called *translation*. Although it would look the same, its co-ordinates would change.

Can you name the shape *ABCD*?

N/A

ABCD is an isosceles trapezium

MATHSFACT

The number 9 is very special. If you take any number, shuffle its digits to make a new number, then find the difference, the digits of the answer will always add up to a multiple of nine! (e.g. 623 − 236 = 387; 3 + 8 + 7 = 18). Furthermore, all multiples of nine have a digit sum which is also a multiple of nine. What are the ninths as decimals?

11+

● You need to be able to add and subtract negative numbers in context, and sort them into order of size.

REAL-LIFE NEGATIVES

Where do we find negative numbers in everyday life? Temperatures are perhaps the most common, but we also talk about negative or overdrawn bank balances (in the red), as well as distances below sea level.

BRR! BELOW ZERO

Negative temperatures mean ice and snow. $^-3$ °C is 3 degrees below zero and so on. Let's extend the number line downwards to see what's going on.

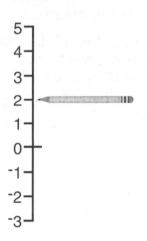

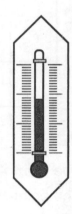

Put your pencil on 2 °C (as shown).

Now move down 3 degrees and you should end up with your pencil on $^-1$ °C.

We write: $2 - 3 = {}^-1$

Check also that: $5 - 8 = {}^-3$

Adding takes us back up again.

$^-2 + 6 = 4$

---

adding or subtracting negative numbers

Adding $^-1$ is equivalent to subtracting 1
$5 + {}^-8$ is equivalent to $5 - 8 = {}^-3$
Subtracting $^-1$ is equivalent to adding 1
$10 - {}^-4$ is equivalent to $10 + 4 = 14$

N/A

PUTTING NEGATIVE NUMBERS IN ORDER

Remember to think of the number line all the time. That way you will correctly say:

$^-15$ is less than $^-8$ which is less than 3 which is less than 11 and so on.

MATHSFACT

The Roman numeral for 10 is *X* and for 5 is *V*. It is thought that *V* represented an open hand with the four fingers together, and that *X* therefore represented two hands.

11+

● You need to be able to draw 3-D objects on paper and construct the nets of simple solids.

HOW TO DRAW A CUBOID

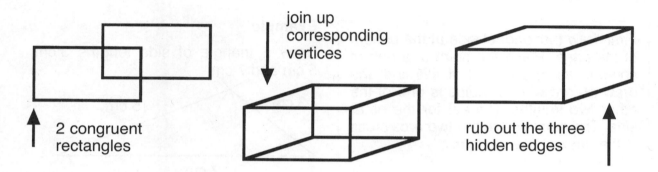

2 congruent rectangles

join up corresponding vertices

rub out the three hidden edges

The most important rule is to make sure lines are parallel. In the middle diagram above there are three sets of parallel lines. *(See also page 56.)*

NETS

A net is a cardboard cut-out which can be folded up to make a solid shape. Here are three common examples:

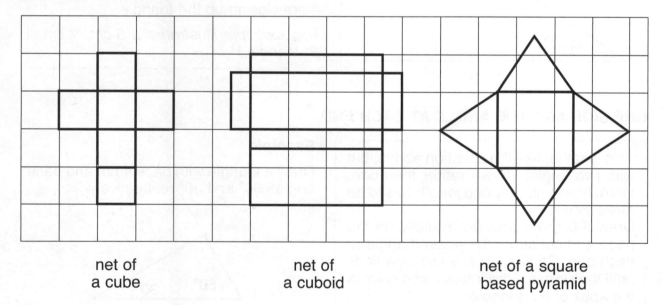

net of
a cube

net of
a cuboid

net of a square
based pyramid

S

MATHSFACT

It is very easy to multiply some 2-digit numbers by 11. Just add the two digits together and write the answer in between (e.g. 36 × 11 = 396). For the other two-digit numbers, carry one on the left digit (e.g. 57 × 11 = 627 not 5127).

TRIANGLES UNDER CONSTRUCTION

11+

• You need to be able to draw accurate scale diagrams (to within one millimetre and one degree) and to be able to construct triangles using just the information given.

THREE SIDES

First draw the longest side at the bottom of the page. Place the point of a pair of compasses at one end of this line and draw an arc whose radius is one of the other two lengths. Repeat for the other side. The point where the two arcs cross is the apex of the triangle.

Example

Draw a triangle of side lengths 3 cm, 5 cm and 7 cm.

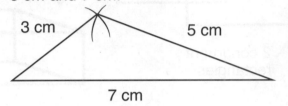

TWO SIDES AND THE ANGLE BETWEEN THEM

Example

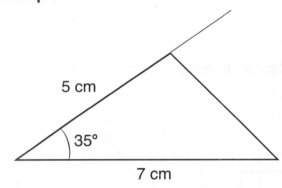

Draw the longer of the two sides horizontally on the page and measure out the given angle at one end. Extend this second side a little further than you think you will need. Now measure along this second side for the correct distance before closing up the triangle.

(This example illustrates a 5 cm, 7 cm, 35° triangle.)

ONE SIDE AND THE ANGLE AT EACH END

S

This is rather like the situation above, but with two angles drawn rather than one. Here, however, only one length has to be measured.

Draw the given side horizontally on the page and construct the desired angle at each end. Continue these two new lines until they cross – the intersection point is the apex of the triangle.

Example

Draw a triangle with base 4 cm and base angles 60° and 30° respectively.

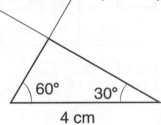

MATHSFACT

Counting in twelves (the duodecimal system) makes a lot more sense than counting in tens, because it is so much easier to include thirds and quarters. This is why we have 12 inches = 1 foot and, at one time, had 12 pennies = 1 shilling.

11+

● You need to understand the difference between reflection and rotation symmetry and know the meaning of the phrase *congruent shapes*.

REFLECTION (REFLECTIVE) SYMMETRY

This happy face has only one line of reflection symmetry (one mirror line).

You could place a mirror down the middle and see the hidden half of the picture in the reflection.

This would **not** work if you placed the mirror any other way.

ROTATION (ROTATIONAL) SYMMETRY

These four strange birds are arranged in a pattern which has rotation symmetry. Here the symmetry is *4-fold* or *order 4* because there are four right ways up with this picture.

Another way of thinking of this is to see that the pattern fits exactly onto itself in four ways.

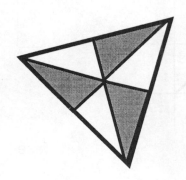

This triangle has **no** mirror lines, but it does have three-fold rotation symmetry. The mirror lines don't work because of the way the triangle is shaded.

CONGRUENCE

Two shapes are described as congruent if one is an exact copy of the other. It doesn't matter if one is rotated or reflected, provided the size and shape of both are identical. (If only the sizes are different, we say that the shapes are *similar*.)

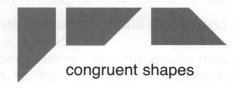

congruent shapes

S

MATHSFACT

The word *TRISKAIDEKAPHOBIC* describes someone who is afraid of the number 13. The superstition apparently goes back to ancient times.

IS A LAZY DOG JUST A SLOPE UP...?

● You need to be able to complete reflections in diagonal lines, sloping either up or down (45°).

Our eyes are good at looking at symmetry which is lateral (left-right) but we find it much harder if it goes up or down (vertical). When it comes to symmetry on a diagonal, many of us would prefer to run away screaming. Yet there's a cunning plan, Baldrick would say. Just pretend it's left-right symmetry!

That's not so crazy, actually. Just turn the paper through 45° and the symmetry line is now vertical! If the symmetry line is now horizontal then you turned it the wrong way. Go back and turn it in the other direction!

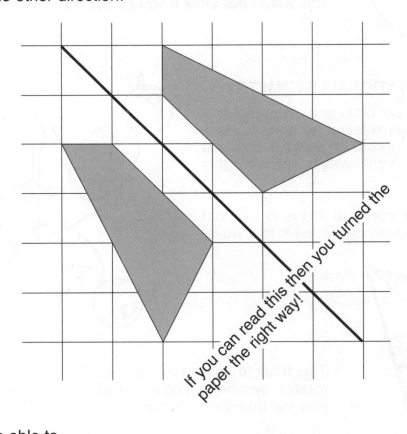

If you can read this then you turned the paper the right way!

You need to be able to

- see when a shape or pattern has a diagonal line of symmetry
- complete a shape or pattern so that it has diagonal symmetry.

In both cases, turning the page makes it all very straightforward.
One good turn deserves another, after all.

MATHSFACT

The word *fortnight* is just a contraction of the phrase *fourteen nights*. You need 14 balls to make a square-based pyramid three layers high. 14 is the first number requiring three different Roman numerals: XIV.

14

SCALE PRACTICE

- You should be familiar with all the common scales used for measuring and know how to read them.

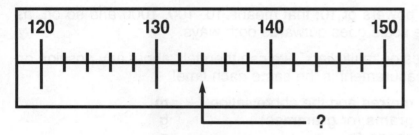

In this first example, we can see that the scale is going up in tens, using intervals of two. This arrow is therefore pointing to **134**

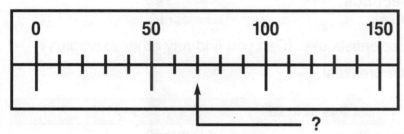

This one goes up in fifties, so each division is worth 10. The arrow here therefore points to **70**

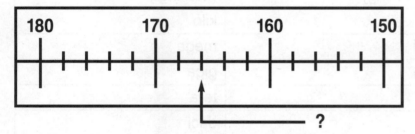

Attention! This one is going down not up! The scale is marked in tens and divided into twos, so the arrow here is pointing to **166**

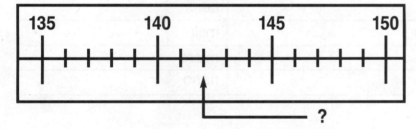

This scale is simply going up in fives, with each division representing one. The arrow here is therefore pointing to **142**

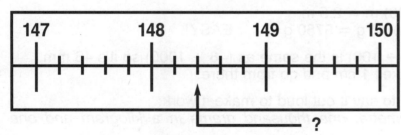

Finally a decimal scale: each unit is divided into 5 divisions, so each one represents 0.2 units.
(1 ÷ 5) The arrow here is pointing to **148.4**

S

MATHSFACT

The process of measuring goes back many thousands of years. The first to be standardised was weight (including money), then length, then the others. Even so, measuring was very approximate, so cheating was common!

METRICS OF THE TRADE

11+

> ● You need to know about common metric units and how to convert between them.

The metric system is based on powers of 10; that means 10, 100, 1000 and so on, as well as 0.1, 0.01, 0.001 etc. The scale goes outwards both ways.

Using a simple system of prefixes or 'multipliers', we can then talk about any position on this scale. The actual unit of measurement is the same each time!

For **length** we use **metres** and the abbreviation **m**
For **mass** **grams** (or **grammes**) **g**
For **time** **seconds** **s**
For **capacity** **litres** **l**

and there are a few others which scientists use. [Can you find any other examples?]

Now for those oh-so-important little prefixes!

effect	put this in front	say this
× 1	{nothing}	{nothing!}
× 1 000	k	kilo
× 1 000 000	M	mega
× 1 000 000 000	G	giga
× 1 000 000 000 000	T	tera
÷ 10	d	deci
÷ 100	c	centi
÷ 1 000	m	milli
÷ 1 000 000	µ	micro
÷ 1 000 000 000	n	nano

Now let's try it out!
250 cm is the same as (250 ÷ 100) m = 2.5 m
5.75 kg is the same as (5.75 × 1000) g = 5750 g   EASY!

Write 4.8 cm in mm like this: (4.8 ÷ 100) is the same as (48 ÷ 1000) so it's 48 mm.
Or just remember that 10 mm makes 1 cm and go from there.

S

This is silly but it helps! You have to say it out loud to make it work:
'One thousand metres in a kilometre, one thousand grams in a kilogram and one thousand whales in a killer whale...'

> **MATHSFACT**
>
> 16 is 2 to the power of 4, i.e. 2 to the power of 2 to the power of 2 It is the number of different results when tossing four coins, and the volume of a hypercube (4-D cube) of side length 2 units.

● You need to be familiar with metric and imperial units in common use, and know how to estimate the answer to complicated calculations.

COMMON UNITS

It is a very useful skill to be able to make reasonable estimates, both of measurements and calculations. This page should improve your reliability!

to estimate	think of
millimetre	window glass 3 mm thick
centimetre	width of little finger
inch	two fingers
foot	adult foot
yard	child's arm span
metre	doorway 2 m high
mile	15-minute walk
kilometre	3-minute bike ride
millilitre	medicine spoon, 5 ml
pint	pint of milk
litre	carton of orange juice

to estimate	think of
gram	milk bottle top, 3 g
ounce	egg, 2 oz
pound	three or four apples
kilogram	bag of sugar
stone	two house bricks
hundredweight	older child's weight
metric tonne	small car
ton	Range Rover, 3 tons
square cm	postage stamp, 5 sq cm
square yard	floor carpet, 20 sq yd
square metre	4 paving slabs

(See reference section page 86 for metric-imperial conversions.)

MATHSFACT

Taking into account all possible combinations of reflection and rotation of a basic pattern, it has been shown that there are only 17 mathematically different types of wallpaper.

PERIMETER, AREA AND VOLUME

● You need to know the difference between these three words, and to be able to determine them in simple cases.

PERIMETER – UNITS OF LENGTH, e.g. cm, m

Perimeter is the distance round the edge of a shape. Think of a fly walking all the way round it. How far would the fly walk?

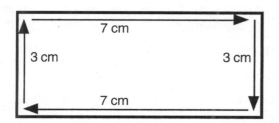

perimeter

= 7 + 3 + 7 + 3

= 20 cm

'Perimeter' contains the word 'rim'!

AREA

Area means counting squares inside the shape. If each square is 1 cm wide we say 'square cm'. We usually measure in units of square cm, square m or square km.

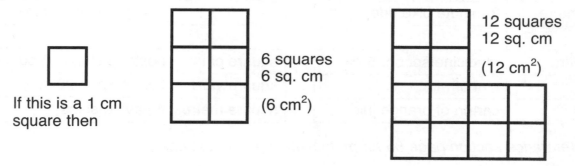

If this is a 1 cm square then

6 squares
6 sq. cm

(6 cm^2)

12 squares
12 sq. cm

(12 cm^2)

VOLUME

Volume can be thought of as cubes inside a solid shape. We often count in cubic centimetres (a cube 1 cm each way), but cubic metres are also useful.

Each cube in this cuboid box is one cubic centimetre.

It has two layers, each of 12 cubes (4 × 3).

So the volume of the box is:

2 × 12 = 24 cubic cm (24 cm^3).

MATHSFACT

There is an anonymous 14th-century manuscript which describes itself as a 'Tretis of Geometri wherby you may knowe the heghte (height), depnes (depth), and the brede (breadth) of mostwhat erthely thynges'.

● You need to be able to describe the position of something using distance and one of the eight compass directions.

THE EIGHT-POINT COMPASS

How do you remember the points of the compass? To start with, *NEWS* is no good because it actually goes *NESW*! Other people have suggested *Naughty Elephants Squirt Water* or even *Nice Easy School Work*! Perhaps the best is simply to remember *North East South West*.

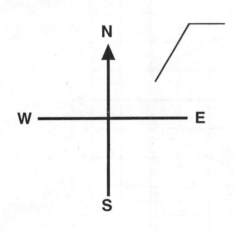

We can then add the diagonals to this to give us four more directions.

Note that the diagonal directions use the two letters either side of them, but always starting with N or S.

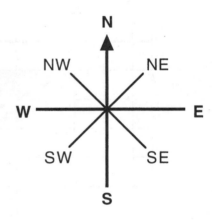

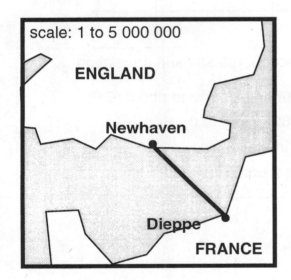

To get from Newhaven to Dieppe, the boat has to sail in a south-east direction for 120 km.

On the way back it sails in a north-west direction for 120 km.

(120 km is about 75 miles.)

S

MATHSFACT

I win more on the National Lottery every month than almost everybody else in the country! Luck? No – I just don't enter! Every week I put my £5 in a jar instead of in the newsagent's. Then every month I get £20! How many people can beat that?

11+

● There are **three** types of transformation which move a shape around without changing its size. You need to be familiar with all three.

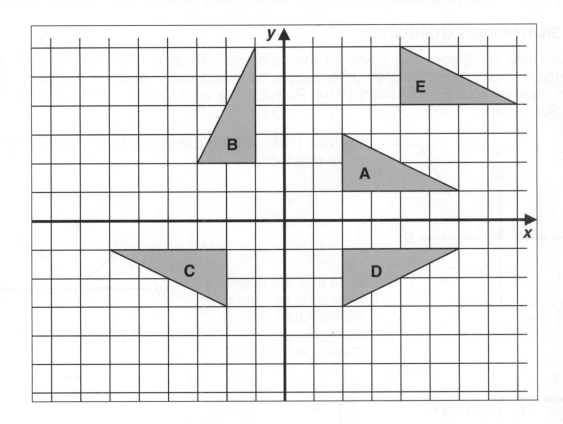

The three transformations used above were reflection, rotation and translation:

to map A on to B the transformation is rotation 90° anti-clockwise about (0,0)

to map A on to C the transformation is rotation 180° about (0,0)

to map A on to D the transformation is reflection in the *x*-axis

to map A on to E the transformation is translation 2 units right and 3 units up

S

MATHSFACT
There are 20 choices for white when moving the first chess piece of the game, and black can similarly reply in any of 20 moves. The first three moves can be played out in over nine million different ways!

WORKING DISCRETELY

> ● You should be able to collect discrete data and organise them using a frequency table.

Discrete data are the sort of data you can count or sort into easy categories. For example, we could ask:

'How many children are in your family?' or 'What is your favourite coloured *Smartie*?'

A frequency table is a good way of collecting and organising discrete data. In this example, we look at the work of a pupil carrying out a survey on favourite breakfast cereals amongst 35 people:

cereal	tally	frequency
corn flakes	⊬⊬ I	
wheat flakes	III	
bran flakes	I	
oat flakes	IIII	

At this stage she had only asked 14 people. Eventually, however, it looked like this:

cereal	tally	frequency
corn flakes	⊬⊬ ⊬⊬ II	12
wheat flakes	⊬⊬ ⊬⊬	10
bran flakes	IIII	4
oat flakes	⊬⊬ IIII	9
	total	35

The pupil has now filled in the frequencies (row totals) and found the overall total. The table is complete.

D

MATHSFACT

Take any three-digit number and multiply it by 7, then by 11, then by 13. What happens? Can you say why this trick works?

11+

- You need to know how to find the mode, median and range of a set of data, and be able to understand their use.

When we have lots of data (information), usually the result of a survey, we need a way of understanding them more clearly. Maths to the rescue! The branch of mathematics which we use for this job is called *statistics*; it is a very useful topic to study.

The modal eye colour here is blue.

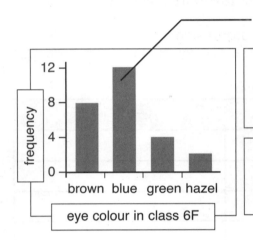

The **mode** is the category in the survey which came up most often, i.e. the one with the greatest frequency. The mode is the most common, or most popular choice.

The **median** means *middle value*. If we sort out our numerical data into order, the median is the value in the middle, or halfway between the middle two, if the number of items of data is even.

The **range** tells us how spread out numerical results are. It is simply the difference between the smallest and largest values in the data.

Example

I put the question 'How many children are in your family?' to 41 different families, and received these answers (sorted into increasing order of size):

1,1,1,1,1,1,1,1,2,2,2,2,2,2,2,2,2,2,2,2,③,3,3,3,3,3,3,3,3,3,4,4,4,4,4,4,4,5,5,5,6

half-way point

So the mode is 2 (most common), the median is 3 (half way through the list), and the range is 5 (since 6 − 1 = 5).

D

MATHSFACT

If you really did win a million pounds one day, then you could live in luxury and never spend a penny of it! Just stick it in a savings account and only spend the interest, which would give you over £80 000 pounds a year!

11+

● You need to be able to calculate the mean of discrete data, and to use your knowledge of averages to compare two distributions.

HOW TO FIND THE MEAN

This is one of the simplest calculations in statistics. All you do is add up your data and divide by the number of items in the list.

Example

Find the mean of the following pupil masses (all in kg):

> 42, 37, 39, 40, 45, 37, 35, 49, 36, 43

Add them up.

> 42 + 37 + 39 + 40 + 45 + 37 + 35 + 49 + 36 + 43 = 403

There are ten pupils in this set of data so we divide by 10

> 403 ÷ 10 = 40.3

Thus the mean pupil mass is **40.3 kg**.

COMPARING TWO DISTRIBUTIONS

Recall (*page 22*) that we can also find the mode, median and range of a set of numerical data. When comparing two distributions, we should take them all into consideration.

Example

A cricket team needs 25 runs in order to win. A choice has to be made between two players whose past run totals look like this:

> Arthur: 19, 24, 30, 27, 23, 24, 29, 21, 31, 25
>   mean 25.3   median 24.5   range 12
>
> Daley: 8, 48, 22, 32, 19, 42, 7, 59, 0, 18
>   mean 25.5   median 20.5   range 59

 >**CHECK**

So whom should they choose? Daley certainly has a greater mean, but he is very inconsistent (large range) and the median tells us that over half his previous games fell short of the desired 25 runs. Arthur, on the other hand, although he has a lower mean, is a much more consistent player (small range), and the median shows us that he had as many results above 25 as below it.

Whom would **you** choose?

D

MATHSFACT

If there are 23 or more people in a room then there is a greater than 50% chance that two of them will share the same birthday.

11+

> • You should understand the importance of using equal class intervals when organising data into groups for making a frequency diagram.

USING GROUPED DATA

Junior Splash Swimming Club recently asked its 55 members how many lengths they swam last weekend. The raw data results were as follows:

14	31	54	40	22	45	57	26	33	56	52
34	24	37	33	36	27	36	34	23	60	29
47	47	57	21	17	37	22	11	32	23	44
32	25	41	42	38	29	44	25	38	39	23
43	46	50	36	38	26	44	33	33	52	34

To make it easier to follow, we group the data:

number of lengths	tally	frequency
0 to 9		0
10 to 19	III	3
20 to 29	ℍℍ ℍℍ IIII	14
30 to 39	ℍℍ ℍℍ ℍℍ IIII	19
40 to 49	ℍℍ ℍℍ I	11
50 to 59	ℍℍ II	7
60 to 69	I	1
	total	55

Note the equal class intervals (10 lengths each). It is now much clearer that the modal class is 30 to 39 lengths.

From the original data, the range is 49 (60−11) lengths. We cannot find the median of grouped data, but we can see that it will be somewhere in the 30 to 39 lengths group. In this case, there are 17 who swam fewer than 30 lengths and 19 who swam more than 39 lengths. If we wanted to find it more accurately, we would have to sort the original data.

D

> **MATHSFACT**
>
> The word *billion* at one time meant 1 000 000 000 if you lived in the USA or France, but (from 1484 onwards) 1 000 000 000 000 if you lived in England or Germany. The smaller American version is used today.

11+

● You need to be able to interpret data presented as a line graph, and be able to read values from it.

TEMPERATURE AND OTHER TIME GRAPHS

One type of line graph consists of short line segments joined up to show how something is changing over a period of time. Here is a temperature graph:

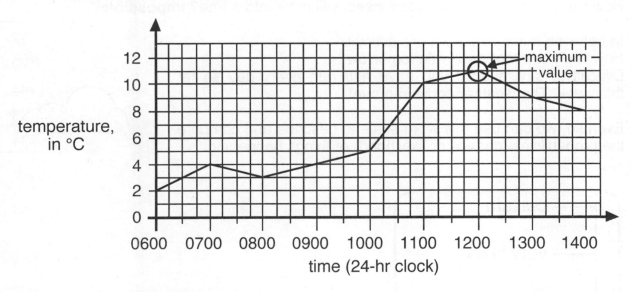

The temperature was measured and plotted every hour, on the hour. The line segments joining these points are really only guesses at the intermediate values – the real change is likely to have been a smooth **curve** throughout the day, but the graph is still a useful way of displaying the collected information.

CONVERSION GRAPHS

Another type of graph is the conversion graph. The one on the right converts between pounds (£) and dollars ($). Check that £5 = $8

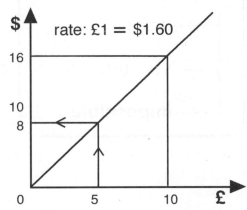

When drawing conversion graphs, it is important to choose a suitable scale. Choose one that is big enough to read accurately, but do use the squares on the graph paper sensibly.

Oh, yes – don't forget to label the axes!

D

MATHSFACT

Have you ever completed a 9×9 Sudoku puzzle? If so, you would be looking at only one of 6 670 903 752 021 072 936 960 possible Sudoku grids.

11+

- When describing and comparing the likelihood of future events, you need to be able to use the common words associated with probability.

HOW LIKELY?

How likely is it that the sun will rise tomorrow morning? **Certain**!

How likely is it that your pet stick insect will grow into a tree? **Impossible**!

In-between questions are more difficult.
How likely is it that it will rain tomorrow?
Difficult to say, even if you have had rain every day so far this week. The weather could improve!

Even so, we can use this word scale to describe and compare the probabilities (chance or likelihood) of things happening:

certain

very likely

likely

even chance

unlikely

very unlikely

impossible

Heads I win, tails you lose...

D

MATHSFACT
The 26 letters in the alphabet are so arranged that the consonants only appear in groups of 3 or 5:
BCD, FGH, JKLMN, PQRST and VWXYZ.

> ● You need to be able to multiply and divide any number by 10 or 100 or 1000 without a calculator.

(First remind yourself of the basics on page 1.)

13+

QUICK SUMMARY OF THIS PAGE

Rule 1: Multiplying by 10 moves the decimal point **right** (or the digits **left**).
Rule 2: Dividing by 10 moves the decimal point **left** (or the digits **right**).

× 100	is	× 10	done twice
× 1000	is	× 10	done three times
÷ 100	is	÷ 10	done twice
÷ 1000	is	÷ 10	done three times

Examples

2.7	÷	10	=	0.27		1.23	×	10	=	12.3
2.7	÷	100	=	0.027		1.23	×	100	=	123
2.7	÷	1000	=	0.0027		1.23	×	1000	=	1230
0.05	×	10	=	0.5		98.7	÷	10	=	9.87
0.05	×	100	=	5		98.7	÷	100	=	0.987
0.05	×	1000	=	50		98.7	÷	1000	=	0.0987

It is an extremely bright idea to make up lots of examples with your calculator. You'll soon be able to get 100% correct!

N/A

MATHSFACT
Zero was a late addition to the number family. It first appeared in India in the ninth century, and was probably a Hindu invention.

TAKE YOUR DECIMAL PLACES

> ● You need to be able to multiply and divide decimals to two decimal places without a calculator.

This is very similar to working with whole numbers – once you can do one you can do the other.

MULTIPLYING

1. Add together the **numbers** of decimal places in the two numbers being multiplied.
2. Rewrite the questions without the decimal points.
3. Multiply the whole numbers in the usual way. *(See also page 37.)*
4. Count back the correct number of decimal places and put the decimal point in the answer.

Example (multiplying decimals)

Calculate 2.3 × 4.76 without using a calculator.

2.3 × 4.76

1 d.p.   2 d.p.   Total: 3 decimal places

$$\begin{array}{r} 476 \\ \times\ 23 \\ \hline 1428 \\ 9520 \\ \hline 10{\cdot}948 \end{array}$$

Rewrite and calculate as a long multiplication without the decimal points.

Count back three places and rewrite the decimal point, giving the final answer **10.948**

DIVIDING

1. Write the division as a fraction, with one number above the other.
2. Multiply top and bottom by 10 (if either number is to 1 d.p.) or by 100 (if either number is to 2 d.p.).
3. Cancel down the fraction in the usual way to simplify it as much as possible.

Example (dividing decimals)

Calculate 3.15 ÷ 4.2

First write as a fraction $\dfrac{3.15}{4.2} \times \dfrac{100}{100} = \dfrac{315}{420}$

Notice that we multiply top and bottom by 100 because the first number has two decimal places. Now cancel down to produce the simplified answer.

$$\frac{315}{420} \xrightarrow{\text{cancel 3s}} \frac{105}{140} \xrightarrow{\text{cancel 5s}} \frac{21}{28} \xrightarrow{\text{cancel 7s}} \frac{3}{4}$$

> ### MATHSFACT
> The word *decimal* means *tenth part* as each place value is one tenth of its left-hand neighbour. Our decimal system therefore does not necessarily refer to non-whole numbers, but to the fact that we count in powers of 10

CLASSIC JURASSIC WITH MINUS THE DINOSAUR

> ● You need to be able to handle 'abstract' questions with negatives – that means with no story attached!

Allow me to introduce Minus the Dinosaur.

And here is the same picture minus the dinosaur:

Minus the Dinosaur can actually do calculations in his head.
He uses this set of rules to deal with positive and negative numbers:

- adding a **positive** is just ordinary adding
- adding a **negative** is equivalent to subtracting
- subtracting a **positive** is just ordinary subtracting
- subtracting a **negative** is equivalent to adding

Let's try a few questions and ask Minus the Dinosaur to help with the answers.

$12 + {}^-3$ is the same as $12 - 3 = 9$
$12 - {}^-3$ is the same as $12 + 3 = 15$
${}^-5 + {}^-4$ is the same as ${}^-5 - 4 = {}^-9$
${}^-5 - {}^-4$ is the same as ${}^-5 + 4 = {}^-1$

Oh, and Minus the Dinosaur agrees with us so we can pat each other on the back.
On second thoughts…

MATHSFACT
Negative numbers have been used in some form for centuries but the notation was difficult and many mathematicians considered them absurd! They have existed in their present form at least as far back as Cardan (1545).

● You need to be able to multiply and divide using various combinations of positive and negative numbers.

POSITIVE OR NEGATIVE?

13+

To put it simply, numbers below zero are negative, and numbers above zero are positive. Negative numbers always have that little negative sign (-) in front of them to show everybody who they are.

MULTIPLICATION WITH NEGATIVE NUMBERS

We know that when we multiply two positive numbers we get a positive answer, so it would seem likely that if we multiplied a positive by a **negative** number, the answer would change to negative too. And that's what happens.

$7 \times 4 = 28$

$7 \times -4 = {}^-28$

$^-3 \times 8 = {}^-24$ The same is true if we multiply a negative number by a positive number.

Predictably, perhaps, multiplying a negative number by another negative number makes the answer positive again.

$-5 \times -9 = 45$

DIVISION WITH NEGATIVE NUMBERS

$72 \div {}^-8 = {}^-9$

$^-56 \div 7 = {}^-8$

$^-16 \div {}^-2 = 8$

This follows very similar rules to the above section on multiplication. A positive number divided by a negative number, or vice versa, gives a negative answer, but one negative number divided by another makes the answer positive.

SUMMARY

N/A

We can put all this information into a table which works for both multiplication and division.

multiply or divide **this** ⟶ **by this** ↓	positive	negative
positive	**+**	**−**
negative	**−**	**+**

MATHSFACT

Although a dodecahedron has 12 faces (each one a regular pentagon) and an icosahedron has 20 faces (each one an equilateral triangle), they both have the same number of edges: 30

THE PRIME OF LIFE

- You need to know how to express any number as a product of its prime factors.

Of course, you can't go much further unless you know what the prime numbers are. Check the table on page 81 in the Reference section of the book, or at least remember that the first five primes are 2, 3, 5, 7 and 11

PROCEDURE

1. If you can, divide by 2 and keep dividing by 2 as many times as possible.
2. Then divide by 3 as many times as possible.
3. Then divide by 5, 7, 11 etc. in turn, each as many times as possible until you reach the answer 1
4. Write the original number as a product of all the primes that went into it, in order.

2	120
2	60
2	30
3	15
5	5
	1

$120 = 2 \times 2 \times 2 \times 3 \times 5$
$120 = 2^3 \times 3 \times 5$

2	210
3	105
5	35
7	7
	1

$210 = 2 \times 3 \times 5 \times 7$

3	243
3	81
3	27
3	9
3	3
	1

$243 = 3 \times 3 \times 3 \times 3 \times 3$
$243 = 3^5$

3	225
3	75
5	25
5	5
	1

$225 = 3^2 \times 5^2$

2	144
2	72
2	36
2	18
3	9
3	3
	1

$144 = 2^4 \times 3^2$

These last two examples (225 and 144) illustrate an important point:
if the prime factors all appear with even powers, then the original number was a square number and vice versa.

The **highest common factor (HCF)** of 12 and 20 is 4 because this is the biggest number which divides into 12 **and** 20 exactly.
The **lowest common multiple (LCM)** of 12 and 20 is 60 because this is the lowest multiple of **both** numbers.

MATHSFACT

In the *Tower of Hanoi* puzzle, discs are moved between three pillars one at a time without putting a large disc on top of a smaller one. If five discs are used, it takes a minimum of 31 moves in order to transfer them all from one pillar to another. With 20 discs it takes over one million moves to complete!

A AS A FRACTION OF *B*

> ● You need to be able to compare two numbers using fractions and percentages.

This method is so easy it's almost like cheating!

Example

A gardener planted 30 seeds and 12 failed to germinate. What is this as a fraction?

What is 12 as a fraction of 30? Simple! $\frac{12}{30}$ That's it!

Now we can simplify this fraction in order to write it in its lowest terms:

$$\frac{12}{30} \xrightarrow{\div 2 \text{ top \& bottom}} \frac{6}{15} \xrightarrow{\div 3 \text{ top \& bottom}} \frac{2}{5}$$

In general, to write *A* as a fraction of *B*, just write it as $\frac{A}{B}$ and simplify as we did above.

PERCENTAGES

You want it as a percentage? Your wish is my cliché! Just make the fraction out of 100

$$\frac{2}{5} \xrightarrow{\times 2 \text{ top \& bottom}} \frac{4}{10} \xrightarrow{\times 10 \text{ top \& bottom}} \frac{40}{100} \xrightarrow{\text{which is}} 40\%$$

Remember that the **original** value or amount is the one which we call 100% when working out profits and discounts, or increases and decreases.

Example

A dress is reduced in a sale from £18 to £14.40

What is this as a percentage?

A reduction from £18 to £14.40 is a reduction of £3.60 on the original amount of £18 As a percentage of £18 this is calculated as follows:

$$\frac{3.60}{18.00} \xrightarrow{\times 100 \text{ top \& bottom}} \frac{360}{1800} \xrightarrow{\div 18 \text{ top \& bottom}} \frac{20}{100} \xrightarrow{\text{which is}} 20\%$$

> **MATHSFACT**
> If you save one penny on 1 January, 2p on the 2nd, 4p on the 3rd, and so on, doubling each time, then by 27 January you will be a millionaire!

FRACTION ACTION: PENCIL AND PAPER

> ● You have to know how to calculate a fraction or a percentage of a quantity without a calculator.

Remember that a fraction is simply a division into equal portions. To find a fraction of something, then you simply have to divide the quantity up into the correct number of portions, and then take the number of portions which are required.

Example (using fractions)

Find $\frac{3}{4}$ of £1.80

The first thing to notice is that we want to divide the money into four equal portions (quarters); then we want three of these portions.

To find $\frac{1}{4}$ of £1.80 we simply divide it by 4. Always **d**ivide by the **d**enominator!

$$\begin{array}{r} 0.45 \\ 4\overline{)1.80} \end{array}$$

so $\frac{1}{4}$ of £1.80 is 45p.

Now, $\frac{3}{4}$ is 3 lots of $\frac{1}{4}$,

therefore $\frac{3}{4}$ of £1.80 is £1.35 (3 × 45p).

Memory aid: DIVIDE by the DENOMINATOR, then TIMES by the TOP.

An easy trick with percentages is to base all your working around the calculation of 10% which is simple to find since it is just one-tenth. 5% is then half of it, 20% is double it and so on.

Example (using percentages)

Find 35% of 140 kg.

	10% of 140 kg is 14 kg (one tenth).
Therefore:	5% of 140 kg is 7 kg (half of 10%).
	30% of 140 kg is 42 kg (3 × 10%).
Therefore:	35% of 140 kg is 49 kg (5% + 30%).

Another trick is to use percentages of 100 which, of course, don't even need to be worked out! If you want to find 36% of 50 cm, just use the fact that 36% of 100 cm is 36 cm, and then halve it to get 18 cm. Similarly, to find 17% of 200, just say '17% of 100 is 17', and then it's clear that 17% of 200 must be 34

> **MATHSFACT**
>
> The word *percent* – short for *per centum* – means *out of 100*. It is interesting therefore to note that the % sign is made from a 1 and two 0s.

> ● You need to understand different ways of calculating with ratios.

13+

It often helps to think of ratios as parts, and to begin by seeing how many parts are involved altogether. That way they become fractions.

Example 1

Share £42 in the ratio 2 : 5

2 parts + 5 parts = 7 parts altogether, so each part is $\frac{1}{7}$ of £42, in other words £6

Answer: 2 parts = 2 × £6 and 5 parts = 5 × £6

So £42 shared in the ratio 2 : 5 is £12 : £30

Example 2

A class contains boys and girls in the ratio 3 : 2

If there are 12 girls, how many boys are there?

First be clear that because of the order of the words, the 3 in the ratio goes with *boys* and the 2 goes with *girls*. Now we are told that the 2 in the ratio represents 12 girls, so each part of the ratio represents 6 children.

Answer: The number of boys is 3 (from the ratio) multiplied by 6 (the number of children per part). So there are 18 boys in the class.

ADAPTING A RECIPE

Sometimes you have to change the quantities in a recipe so that it serves a different number of people. Ratios to the rescue!

Example 3

N/A

| *Apple Pie (serves 4)*
200 g shortcrust pastry
480 g cooking apples
120 g brown sugar
4 cloves | Adapt this recipe for 4 people to serve 5 people. |  | *Apple Pie (serves 5)*
250 g shortcrust pastry
600 g cooking apples
150 g brown sugar
5 cloves |

We first calculate one person's share (dividing by 4) and then multiply this by 5, as has been done above. This method is called the *unitary method*, and can be used for either increases or decreases.

> **MATHSFACT**
>
> If you arrange the numbers 1 to 16 to make a magic square (every row, column and diagonal giving the same total), then that total will always be 34. There are 880 different ways of achieving this!

TIME TO ORDER A ROUND

13+

- You need to be able to put decimal numbers in order and round them to any number of decimal places.

ORDERING DECIMALS

This is made much easier by remembering that you can always write zeros at the right-hand end of any decimal number without changing its value.

> 0.5   is the same as   0.50   and   0.500   and   0.5000   and ...

Example

Sort these numbers into increasing order of size:

> 2.71,   0.721,   0.17,   0.7,   1.271,   1.72

1. Ignore the decimal parts of each number initially and put them in whole number order.

   0.721,   0.17,   0.7,   1.271,   1.72,   2.71

2. Make all the decimal parts the same length by writing extra zeros where necessary.

   0.721,   0.170,   0.700,   1.271,   1.720,   2.710

3. Sort the decimal parts without disturbing the whole number order.

   0.170,   0.700,   0.721,   1.271,   1.720,   2.710

4. Remove the extra zeros.

   0.17,   0.7,   0.721,   1.271,   1.72,   2.71

With practice you will develop your own short cuts to this procedure, until you can do the entire sort in your head. It's a handy little skill to acquire!

ROUNDING TO TWO DECIMAL PLACES

Draw a vertical line after the second decimal place to separate the second and third positions. If the number after the line is 5 or more, then round **up**. If the number after the line is 4 or less, then round **down**.

> Round **up**: add 1 to the digit **before** the vertical line.
> Round **down**: remove all digits **after** the vertical line. Don't do anything else!

N/A

$$3.24|\textcircled{7}1 \rightarrow 3.25$$

$$2.47|\textcircled{1}3 \rightarrow 2.47$$

Similarly:

2.95 → 3.0 to 1 d.p.

2.71818 → 2.7182 to 4 d.p.

MATHSFACT

For those who like **really** large numbers, a trillion is a thousand billion (12 zeros); a quadrillion is 1 followed by 15 zeros, while a quintillion has 18 zeros. A googol has 100 zeros, and a googolplex has a googol zeros!

THE LONG AND THE SHORT OF IT

> ● You should be able to multiply and divide two numbers using pencil and paper methods.

Believe me, if you know your tables up to 10 × 10, then you can multiply any two numbers up to 100 × 100. Actually you can multiply any two numbers as big as you like! (I don't recommend going much past a million though in case you miss dinner.)

Short multiplication usually refers to multiplying by a single-digit number. Long multiplication is used when multiplying by a number with two or more digits. Short division and long division work the same way. (With **division**, obviously!!)

Here's a little tip: 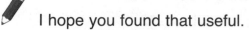   I hope you found that useful.

There are many methods of multiplying two numbers, and you probably know at least two. Look in the following section for some crazy methods which are fun to try.

WHENEVER YOU MULTIPLY OR DIVIDE, ALWAYS MAKE AN ESTIMATE FIRST TO HELP YOU CHECK YOUR ANSWER!

Division always divides people into two groups. Those who get the right answer and those who don't. If you want to be in the first group, here are some things to remember:

- practise by doing a multiplication question 'in reverse'
- you can always get there by repeated subtraction if you're desperate (this method is sometimes known as 'chunking')
- always check your answer by multiplying back again
- check that your answer is close to your original estimate
- you can write any division question as a fraction and just cancel it down until you get your answer

DECIMALS

Those who treat decimals as whole numbers are missing the point. Provided you put that point back again afterwards, though, it's the best way to do them.

How many decimal places do you make in the final answer?
When you **multiply** two decimals, you **add** the number of decimal places.
When you **divide** one decimal by another, you **subtract** the number of decimal places.

Quick example: 6.71 (2 d.p.) and 1.1 (1 d.p.)
　　　　671 × 11 = 7381 so put (2 + 1) 3 decimal places in to get
　　　　6.71 × 1.1 = 7.381
　　　　671 ÷ 11 = 61 so put (2 − 1) 1 decimal place in to get 6.71 ÷ 1.1 = 6.1

> **MATHSFACT**
> Many words from the early Maths text books might today be unfamiliar: *summand + summand = sum; minuend − subtrahend = difference; multiplicator × multiplicand = product; dividend ÷ divisor = quotient.*

$$\frac{6.71}{1.1} = \frac{671}{110}$$

$$110\overline{\smash)671}$$

● You need to be able to multiply a 3-digit number by a 2-digit number without a calculator.

13+

We shall take the example 126 × 64 and work it through, explaining every stage in detail.

PROCEDURE

1. Write the two-digit number underneath the three-digit number, lining up the units column as if it were an addition problem.

```
    1 2 6
×     6 4
```

2. Multiply the three-digit number by the **units** digit of the two-digit number, working from **right** to **left**, carrying where necessary.

```
    1 2 6
×     6 4
    ─────
    5 0 4
    1 2
```

3. Put a zero in the units column of the second row of working. Multiply the three-digit number by the **tens** digit of the two-digit number, again working from **right** to **left**, with carrying if it is needed.

```
    1 2 6
×     6 4
    ─────
    5 0 4
  7 5 6 0
  1 3      ↑
```

4. Add together the two rows of working to obtain the final answer.

```
    1 2 6
×     6 4
    ─────
    5 0 4
  7 5 6 0
  ───────
  8 0 6 4
  1
```

N/A

Notes

You can, if you wish, multiply by the tens digit first, but it is still a good idea to keep two separate rows of working. The reason we write a zero in the units column in step 3 is because we are really multiplying by 60, not by 6, so writing the 0 effectively does the multiplying by 10 for us.

MATHSFACT

Addition was invented as a short cut to counting on one by one; multiplication, which means 'many folds' was designed to 'fold together' many additions.

MULTIFARIOUS MULTIPLICATION METHODS

● It's useful to know a variety of methods for multiplying two numbers using pencil and paper. Here are some interesting ways of finding 387 × 52 which are fun to try.

13+

THE ELIZABETHAN METHOD ('NAPIER'S BONES')

Write the two numbers across the top and down the right. Multiply each pair of digits in the grid. Add along the diagonals and the answer appears around the other corner!

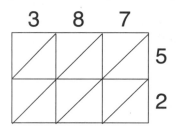
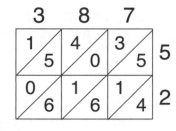
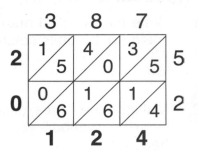

(Add from the right and work backwards. Don't forget those carry digits!)
So 387 × 52 = 20124

THE EGYPTIAN METHOD

Make two columns. On the left write 1 and on the right write the larger number of the two. Keep doubling both. You get your answer by adding a clever selection of the rows.

1	387
2	774
4	**1548***
8	3096
16	**6192***
32	**12384***

I don't need to go any further because doubling again would give me 64 and I don't need to go past 52. Now I choose the rows for which the **left** numbers add up to 52, then add up the numbers on the **right**.

*52 = 32 + 16 + 4 so I just add up 12384 + 6192 + 1548 = 20124 as above.

THE RUSSIAN PEASANT METHOD

N/A

Make two columns, with one number in each column. Double the numbers on the right and halve the numbers on the left (ignoring remainders). At the end, cross out the rows in which there is an **even** number on the left, then add up the remaining numbers on the **right**.

~~52~~	~~387~~
~~26~~	~~774~~
13	1548
~~6~~	~~3096~~
3	6192
1	12384

Now there's a surprise! It's the same numbers left as with the Egyptian method! I wonder why . . .

See how many other methods you can find, and write them in the Notes section at the back of this book.

MATHSFACT

Mathematicians have been looking for ways of multiplying for thousands of years, and they have frequently involved extraordinary procedures. Several methods such as these were described by Pacioli in 1494.

CHECK, MATE

- You should know how to check your answers by using inverses and approximations.

Inverses can be thought of as opposites. There are lots of opposite pairs in mathematics, but let's start with the most important four:

The inverse of this:	$+$	$-$	$\times$	$\div$
is this:	$-$	$+$	$\div$	$\times$

CHECKING USING INVERSES

1. We have just done the calculation: **$257 - 78 = 179$**

   We check the subtraction by **adding**: **$179 + 78 = 257$**   **OK!**

2. We have just done the calculation: **$108 \div 3 = 36$**

   We check the division by **multiplying**: **$36 \times 3 = 108$**   **OK!**

ESTIMATION AND APPROXIMATION

Imagine that on your calculator you are working out: **28.7×5.42**
and you obtain from the calculator display the
answer: **697.554**

A quick approximation will tell you that this can't be right!

28.7 is roughly 30, and 5.42 is roughly 5, so the answer
must be about 150

Better try again!

MATHSFACT
If two perfect computers were challenged to play chess against each other, they would agree a draw on the first move.

THE ANSWER'S IN THE QUESTION

> ● You need to be able to use multiplication and division facts to calculate related problems.

13+

Variations on the original problem are achieved using a combination of two procedures:

1. changing the order of the numbers in the question and answer
2. multiplying or dividing any of the numbers involved by powers of 10 (i.e. by 10 or 100 or 1000 etc.)

Examples 1

Given that $5 \times 7 = 35$, **write down** the answers to the following:
(By saying *write down*, it means that you shouldn't need to do any detailed calculations.)

a) $35 \div 7$ b) 50×700 c) $350 \div 0.05$

Answers

a) $35 \div 7 = 5$ This is just a restatement of the original problem, in a different order.

b) $50 \times 700 = 35\,000$ If the question is multiplied by 10, so is the answer. This has been done three times here: 5×10 and $7 \times 10 \times 10$, so the answer is $35 \times 10 \times 10 \times 10$

c) $350 \div 0.05 = 7000$ First use the fact that $35 \div 5 = 7$ and think of the division as a fraction.

Then $350 \div 5 = 70$	Multiplying the **numerator** by 10 multiplies the answer by 10
$350 \div 0.5 = 700$	Dividing the **denominator** by 10 multiplies the answer by 10
$350 \div 0.05 = 7000$	Dividing the denominator again by 10 multiplies the answer by 10 once more.

Examples 2

Given that $58.7 \times 89 = 5224.3$, **write down** the answers to the following:

a) 5.87×8900 b) $52243 \div 58.7$ c) $5.2243 \div 0.089$

N/A

Answers

a) $5.87 \times 8900 = 52243$ One number has been multiplied by 100 and the other has been divided by 10; the net result of this *tug of war* is $\times 10$

b) $52243 \div 58.7 = 890$ We know that $5224.3 \div 58.7 = 89$ (the original problem). Therefore $52243 \div 58.7$ is 10 times bigger.

c) $5.2243 \div 0.089 = 58.7$ We know that $5224.3 \div 89 = 58.7$ (the original problem). Both numbers in the division have been divided by 1000. If both numbers in a division are multiplied or divided by the same amount, then the answer stays the same. If you think about it, this is what equivalent fractions are all about!

MATHSFACT

Forty is the only number with the letters in alphabetical order.

BRING ON THE SUBSTITUTION

> ● You need to be able to substitute numbers into simple formulae using *BODMAS* correctly, with or without a calculator.

Armed with the knowledge of everything on the previous page, we can now tackle a wide variety of questions involving algebraic substitution. But first we must find out – who or what is *BODMAS*?

most important (do first)	**B**rackets	
	Of (e.g. square or square root of)	
	Division	} equal priority; work from left to right
	Multiplication	
least important (do last)	**A**ddition	} equal priority; work from left to right
	Subtraction	

BODMAS means that there is now no doubt about the answer to ambiguous questions:

$3 + 4 \times 5 = 23$ (not 35) because we work out the 4×5 first.

Your calculator must be a *BODMAS* calculator. Type in the above question to check! (*See also MATHSFACT below.*)

Algebraic examples

1. Given that $p = 2q + 3(q + r)$, find p when $q = 3$, $r = 4$
   $p = 6 + 3 \times 7$ [since $q + r = 7$]
   $p = 27$ [since $3 \times 7 = 21$]

2. Given that $E = mc^2$, find E when $m = 10$ and $c = 5$
   $E = 10 \times 5^2$
   $E = 10 \times 25$
   $E = 250$

MATHSFACT
There are two types of calculator: *LTR* and *MDF*. Type in $10 - 2 \times 3$ and then press *equals*. LTR (Left To Right) gives the answer 24, while MDF (Multiplication and Division First) gives 4. MDF knows about BODMAS. Does yours?

A CRASH COURSE ON SYMBOLS

- You need to know about simple symbolic formulae (one or two step).

A QUICK REVIEW OF THE BASICS

1. **We do not use × (times) or ÷ (division) signs.**

    $$ab \qquad\qquad \frac{a}{b}$$

    means a times b \qquad means a divided by b

2. **Like terms**

    Like terms have exactly the same letter part. The following terms are like pairs:

    3a and 7a \qquad 5b and $^-$2b \qquad 6ab and ab \qquad 3a^2 and 8a^2

3. **Collecting like terms**

    $$\circled{a} + \boxed{5b} - 3ab + \circled{3a} + 4ab - \boxed{b}$$
    $$= 4a + 4b + ab$$

4. **Multiplying out brackets**

    Remember to multiply the number outside by everything in the brackets. And watch the plus and minus signs!

    $3(2a + 5b)$ \qquad $a(b - 2c)$
    $= 6a + 15b$ \qquad $= ab - 2ac$

    > See page 94 for a note about alphabetical order.

5. **Factorising into brackets**

    $4a + 4b$ \qquad $15p^2 - 10pq$
    $= 4(a + b)$ \qquad $= 5p(3p - 2q)$

6. **Equivalent fractions**

    The numerator and denominator must always be divided (or multiplied) by the same number.

    $$\frac{4}{12} \rightarrow \frac{2}{6} \rightarrow \frac{1}{3} \rightarrow \frac{10}{30} \rightarrow \ldots(etc.)$$

7. **Simplifying powers**

    When multiplying, you **add** the powers; when dividing you **subtract** the powers.

    (i) $aa = a^2$ \qquad (ii) $a(a + a^2) = a^2 + a^3$ \qquad (iii) $\dfrac{12a^3}{4a^2} \rightarrow \dfrac{3a^3}{a^2} \rightarrow 3a$

MATHSFACT

The first textbook to mention Algebra in its title was written by the Italian mathematician Bombelli. His *L'Algebra Parte Maggiore Dell' Arimetica* was published in Bologna in 1572.

● You should be familiar with co-ordinates in all four quadrants and know about graph mappings.

The four quadrants are the four regions on the graph formed by extending both the x and y axes into the negative numbers.

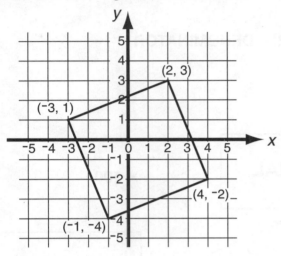

Is this shape

a) a rhombus

b) a square

c) a parallelogram

d) a trapezium

e) a kite

f) a rectangle?

(*answer below*)

MAPPINGS

Graph mappings, or line equations, are usually given in one of the following forms:

	type 1	type 2	type 3	type 4
form	$x = k$	$y = k$	$y = mx$	$y = mx + c$
example	$x = 5$	$y = {}^-3$	$y = 2x$	$y = 2x + 5$

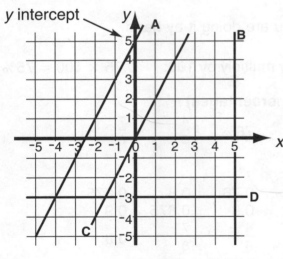

type 1
These are always vertical lines.

type 2
These are always horizontal lines.

type 3
These are always sloping lines going through the origin.

type 4
These are the rest. They slope up or down and cross both axes.

Can you match each of the lines **A**, **B**, **C** and **D** with the correct equation from the examples in the box above?

Q1: all of them!! (sorry!)   Q2: **A** is type 4, **B** is type 1, **C** is type 3 and **D** is type 2

MATHSFACT

René Descartes (1596–1650), French mathematician and philosopher, was responsible for bringing us Cartesian Co-ordinates, the full title of the topic on this page. His work, however, goes way beyond CE standard!

● You need to be able to transfer easily between fractions, decimals and percentages.

13+

Here is a cunning little diagram which has helped many children through the fraction/percentage/decimal maze. I hope it helps you too!

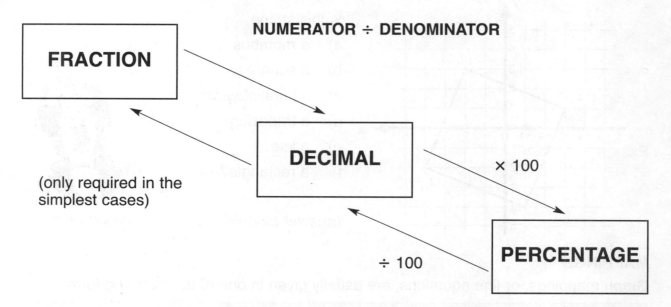

Example 1 (writing a fraction as a decimal and as a percentage)

Write the fraction $\frac{3}{4}$ as a decimal and as a percentage.

$3 \div 4 = 0.75$ or $4\overline{)3.00}^{\,0.75}$ if you are doing it by hand.

Now to write 0.75 as a percentage, we simply multiply by 100: $0.75 \times 100 = \textbf{75\%}$

Example 2 (ordering fractions, decimals and percentages)

N/A

Place in increasing order of size: 0.9   78% $\frac{4}{5}$ $\frac{7}{8}$

Method

Write as decimals:	0.9	0.78	0.8	0.875
Sort the decimals:	0.78	0.8	0.875	0.9
Rewrite as they were:	78%	$\frac{4}{5}$	$\frac{7}{8}$	0.9

MATHSFACT

If you want to send a cheeseburger into space you have to be able to throw it upwards with a speed of at least 40 000 km per hour.

VULGAR, IMPROPER AND DOWNRIGHT RUDE

> ● You need to be able to add, subtract, multiply and divide fractions and mixed numbers.

A REMINDER OF THE BASICS

1. You cannot add or subtract two fractions with different denominators. You must make the denominators the same first.
2. To make two denominators the same, find the smallest number into which both denominators divide (the lowest common multiple or lowest common denominator) and use equivalent fractions to scale up the two fractions accordingly.
3. It is a good idea to convert mixed numbers (whole number part and vulgar fraction part) into improper 'top heavy' fractions before proceeding. Although for addition this is not recommended (*see first example*), it can make subtractions easier; for multiplication and division it's vital.

Example 1 (addition)

$3\frac{3}{4} + 2\frac{4}{5}$ is the same as $5 + \frac{3}{4} + \frac{4}{5}$

Now, $\frac{3}{4} + \frac{4}{5} \rightarrow \frac{15}{20} + \frac{16}{20} = \frac{31}{20}$ or $1\frac{11}{20}$ So $3\frac{3}{4} + 2\frac{4}{5} \rightarrow 5 + 1\frac{11}{20} = 6\frac{11}{20}$

Example 2 (subtraction)

$3\frac{3}{4} - 2\frac{4}{5}$ First change to improper fractions $3\frac{3}{4} - 2\frac{4}{5} = \frac{15}{4} - \frac{14}{5}$

Remember that the denominator stays the same. To find the new numerator, use the word formula:

new numerator = whole number × denominator + old numerator

Then proceed as usual $\frac{15}{4} - \frac{14}{5} \rightarrow \frac{75}{20} - \frac{56}{20} = \frac{19}{20}$

Example 3 (multiplication)

$3\frac{3}{4} \times 2\frac{4}{5} \rightarrow \frac{15}{4} \times \frac{14}{5} \xrightarrow{\text{cancel 5s}} \frac{3}{4} \times \frac{14}{1} \xrightarrow{\text{cancel 2s}} \frac{3}{2} \times \frac{7}{1} = \frac{21}{2}$ or $10\frac{1}{2}$

Example 4 (division)

$3\frac{3}{4} \div 2\frac{4}{5} \rightarrow \frac{15}{4} \div \frac{14}{5} \xrightarrow{\text{invert the second fraction}} \frac{15}{4} \times \frac{5}{14} = \frac{75}{56}$ or $1\frac{19}{56}$

MATHSFACT

The Dutch artist M C Escher (1898-1972) used mathematics in a very clever way in his pictures. By subtly breaking the rules of perspective, for example, he created many 'impossible' buildings. He is equally famous for his skill at tessellating animal shapes to cover the page.

● You need to be able to describe in words the next term of a sequence.

13+

Examples

As a warm-up to this page, write down the next two terms of each of the following sequences:

a)   3, 5, 7, 9, 11, 13, ..., ...

b)   27, 23, 19, 15, 11, 7, ..., ...

c)   2, 3, 5, 8, 12, 17, ..., ...

d)   32, 16, 8, 4, 2, 1, ..., ...   *(Answers below)*

If you got those right, you don't really need to stick around here!

'Describing in words' is when you explain what the sequence is doing. From above:

a)   adding 2 each time

b)   subtracting 4 each time

c)   adding one more than the previous time

d)   dividing by 2 each time.

Remind yourself again of the method described on page 6.

This method (The Difference Method) will show up almost every hidden pattern.

N/A

That's it for this page!

How did you do on those sequences?

(a) 15, 17   (b) 3, −1   (c) 23, 30   (d) 0.5, 0.25

MATHSFACT

The King James version of the Bible was produced in 1610 when William Shakespeare was 46 years old. In Psalm 46, the 46th word is *shake* and the 46th word from the end is *spear*!

> ● You need to be able to describe in words the *n*th term of a sequence where the rule is linear.

It's all very well being able to find the next term in a sequence, but could you find the 10th term, the 100th term, without plodding through all the other terms along the way?

13+

If a sequence is going up or down by the same amount each time, then that number becomes your multiplying number.

Example

Find the 100th term of the sequence: 2, 5, 8, 11, 14, ...

Note that this is going up each time by **three**.

first term:	2	1 × 3 =	3
second term:	5	2 × 3 =	6
third term:	8	3 × 3 =	9
fourth term:	11	4 × 3 =	12

Look at the last column: 3, 6, 9, 12 – it is always one more than the number we want (2, 5, 8, 11).

Multiplying by three is therefore not enough. We then have to subtract one.

TEST

Fifth term should be: 14
Find it by calculation.   **5** × 3 = 15
    15 − 1 = **14** ✓   YES! It works!

Now we can find the 100th term easily.

Hundredth term: **100** × 3 = 300
    300 − 1 = **299**

MATHSFACT

The rhyme for remembering the number of days in the months, beginning *Thirty days has September*, first appeared in English in 1590.

EQUATIONS IN THE BALANCE

● You need to be able to solve simple linear equations.

Many people find it helpful to think of equations as a set of balance scales, with the = sign as the pivot. At every stage of your working, be careful not to upset the balance!

HOW TO SOLVE EQUATIONS: SOME GUIDELINES

1. At every stage apply the same working to both sides of the equation.
2. Think about the order in which the equation was written *(BODMAS may help you)*, and work backwards to the unknown variable by *undoing* each step in reverse order.
3. Try to collect letter terms on one side and number terms on the other.
4. Don't be put off if the answer is negative or a fraction.

Example 1

Solve the equation $4x + 5 = 26 - 3x$

equation	do this to both sides
$4x + 5 = 26 - 3x$	subtract 5
$4x = 21 - 3x$	add $3x$
$7x = 21$	divide by 7
$x = 3$	**check original equation**
(**check LHS**) $4(3) + 5 = 17$	
(**check RHS**) $26 - 3(3) = 17$	**It's the right answer!**

Example 2

Solve the equation $5(19 - x) = 3(3x - 1)$

equation	do this to both sides
$5(19 - x) = 3(3x - 1)$	multiply out the brackets
$95 - 5x = 9x - 3$	add 3
$98 - 5x = 9x$	add $5x$
$98 = 14x$	divide by 14
$7 = x$	**check original equation**
(**check LHS**) $5(19 - 7) = 60$	
(**check RHS**) $3(21 - 1) = 60$	**It's the right answer!**

MATHSFACT

The first '=' sign in print was in mathematician Robert Recorde's *The Whetstone of Witte* (1557). He used 'a paire of paralleles, or gemowe (twin) lines of one length: =, bicause noe 2 thynges, can be moare equalle.'

EQUATION FORMULATION

- You need to be able to form and solve linear equations when solving problems.

At one time, not so long ago, puzzles of the kind below featured frequently in algebra textbooks, much to the pleasure (?) of their students . . .

> I have x sweets. You have three fewer than twice the number I have. One third of your sweets is five fewer than the number I have. How many do we each have?

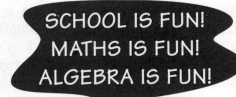

SCHOOL IS FUN!
MATHS IS FUN!
ALGEBRA IS FUN!

Of course this sort of puzzle is easily solved by setting up a simple equation.

We make the equation up step by step:

I have x sweets.

You have three fewer than twice the number I have.

So you have three fewer than twice x

You have $2x - 3$ sweets.

One third of your sweets is five fewer than my number of sweets.

So one third of $(2x - 3)$ is $x - 5$

That's the equation!

$\frac{1}{3}(2x - 3) = x - 5$	Multiply both sides by 3
$2x - 3 = 3x - 15$	Add 15 to both sides.
$2x + 12 = 3x$	Subtract $2x$ from both sides.
$12 = x$	So I had 12 sweets . . .
$2(12) - 3 = 21$	. . . and you had 21

N/A

MATHSFACT

Augustus de Morgan (1806–1871), when asked about his age, replied: 'I was N years old in the year N squared'. Which year was he talking about?

IT'S HIGHLY SIGNIFICANT, JIM

> ● You need to know about rounding numbers, significant figures and approximating.

(First of all turn back to page 35 to remind yourself about rounding decimals.)

13+

In many situations, particularly when interpreting a full calculator display, care has to be taken that the answer quoted is given to an appropriate level of accuracy. What is appropriate? Well, usually the figures in the question indicate the sort of accuracy which is required. For example, finding the circumference of a pond 4.5 m in diameter would not need such an accurate answer as if the pond were given as having a diameter of 4.5126729 m. Common sense is usually the best guide!

SIGNIFICANT FIGURES IN WHOLE NUMBERS

All the figures in a whole number are significant, except sometimes for zeros at the end. Thus 4500 is written to two significant figures, but 4000 is only to one significant figure. Similar ideas for rounding decimals apply when rounding whole numbers.

Example

Round the number 23456 to   (a) 3 significant figures   (b) 2 significant figures.

(Think of the 'circle and line' method used on page 35 when doing these.)

SIGNIFICANT FIGURES IN DECIMALS

All the figures in a decimal are significant, except for zeros at the **beginning**. Thus 0.52 and 0.000052 are both to two significant figures, but 0.00520052 is to six significant figures. (You must include the zeros in the middle.) Similarly, 0.052000 is to **five** significant figures, since only zeros at the beginning are not significant.

Example

My calculator display gives the answer to a problem as 47176.45555
Write this to three significant figures.

Notice that, as with all rounding situations, the result is always the same order of magnitude (rough size) as the original number. Here both numbers are roughly 47000 (to two significant figures). Don't make the common mistake of leaving out the vital zeros at the end. The answer is **not** 472 !!

N/A

APPROXIMATIONS

A quick check on a calculator display can always be made by rounding all the figures in a calculation to one or two significant figures, and then working out the problem mentally. *(See also page 39.)*

47200   (b) 23000   (a) 23500

MATHSFACT

In many ways 50p and 20p coins behave like circles! They have a constant diameter (same length every direction), and so they would make very good rollers. Try putting 2 or 3 between two rulers and sliding the rulers along!

ESTIMATING AND ROUGH ANSWERS

Sometimes we only need an approximate idea of the answer to a question, perhaps because we are in a hurry, or because a calculator is unavailable, or because we want to do a quick mental check of a calculator answer. Whatever the reason, rough answers are very quick to find!

The basic rule is to round each number up or down to the nearest ten, hundred, thousand etc. *(See also* Significant Figures *on page 50.)*

13+

Example

$$\frac{(417.6 \times 2.91)}{(50.8 + 9.73)} \quad \text{becomes} \quad \frac{(400 \times 3)}{(50 + 10)} \rightarrow \frac{1200}{60} = 20$$

This compares well with the exact answer which is .... Well, I'm sure you can work it out for yourself!

$$\frac{1200}{60}$$

SCREEN TEST: INTERPRETING CALCULATOR DISPLAYS

Money, time, distances etc. – we know the difference but the poor calculator doesn't have a clue. It operates a simple RIRO rule (Rubbish In Rubbish Out) which means that it cannot think for itself!

You could ask your calculator to work out £3 + 12 minutes – 4 bananas and it would tell you that the answer was 11, but that's just making the calculator look stupid.

Calculators sometimes give rounding errors, and you need to be careful with money and time answers. Always think of the context of the question.

3.7	£3.70 not 3 pounds and 7 pence
4.25	4.25 hours = 4 hours 15 minutes (not 4 hours 25 minutes)
5.3	If we have worked out how many tins of paint we need then the answer is 6 not 5 since 5 would not be enough!
41.99999999999	This recurring decimal seems to suggest that the real answer is actually 42 after all!

N/A

> **MATHSFACT**
> The British Library receives copies of all books produced in the UK, taking its 150 million item stock up by about 3 million every year.

FRACTION ACTION: CALCULATOR POWER

13+

> ● You have to know how to calculate a fraction or a percentage of a quantity using a calculator.

Did you know that every calculator has an *OF* button? No, not *OFF – OF*.

It looks like this:

'Aha!' You say. He's really gone this time. Yet it's true! Let's see how it works.

USING A FRACTION CALCULATOR

Most fraction calculators have a button which looks something like this:

Let's work out $\frac{2}{3}$ of 72

$$2 \;\; \boxed{a^b/_c} \;\; 3 \;\; \boxed{\times} \;\; 72 \;\; \boxed{=} \;\; \boxed{48.}$$

two-thirds   of   72   equals   48

If we don't have a fraction key on the calculator, we can use the division key instead:

$$2 \;\; \boxed{\div} \;\; 3 \;\; \boxed{\times} \;\; 72 \;\; \boxed{=} \;\; \boxed{48.}$$

two-thirds   of   72   equals   48

PERCENTAGES

Percentages are just as easy. Remember that % means *out of 100* and you have a fraction again, or a decimal if you prefer. We'll find 75% of 108

N/A

$$75 \;\; \boxed{\div} \;\; 100 \;\; \boxed{\times} \;\; 108 \;\; \boxed{=} \;\; \boxed{81.}$$

or simply $$0.75 \;\; \boxed{\times} \;\; 108 \;\; \boxed{=} \;\; \boxed{81.}$$

> **MATHSFACT**
> The 52 cards in a playing card deck can be arranged in 52 ways, which means 52 × 51 × 50 × 49 × ... × 3 × 2 × 1 ways. This number has 68 digits and is bigger than the number of atoms which make up the Earth.

● You need to know and apply the angle laws of straight lines and understand the symmetry of polygons.

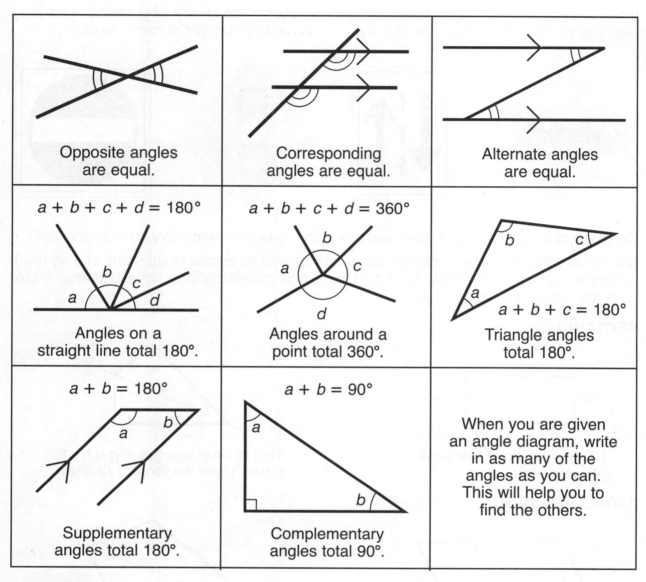

Opposite angles are equal.	Corresponding angles are equal.	Alternate angles are equal.
$a + b + c + d = 180°$	$a + b + c + d = 360°$	
Angles on a straight line total 180°.	Angles around a point total 360°.	$a + b + c = 180°$ Triangle angles total 180°.
$a + b = 180°$	$a + b = 90°$	When you are given an angle diagram, write in as many of the angles as you can. This will help you to find the others.
Supplementary angles total 180°.	Complementary angles total 90°.	

POLYGONS

Most of what you need to know about angles in regular polygons is on page 90. Look out for isosceles triangles! The fact that they have two equal sides and two equal angles can often provide you with lots of clues. All regular polygons (including the equilateral triangle) have both rotation and reflection symmetry. This is always the same as the number of sides. For example, a regular octagon has 8 mirror lines and rotation symmetry of order 8.

MATHSFACT

The word *counter* was used to describe any bead-like object used to assist in doing arithmetic, as far back as 1310. The word came to be used to describe mathematicians, and even the desks where they sat and counted.

13+

● You need to understand reflection symmetry in two-dimensional shapes.

Lines of symmetry, or mirror lines, always go through the centre of a shape. This may help you decide where they are. A shape can have any number of mirror lines.

Only one of the signs above does **not** have any reflection symmetry. Which one is it?

Don't forget that mirror lines can go diagonally as well as across or up (think of a square). However, many people think that rectangles and parallelograms have diagonal mirror lines too – don't be caught out!

RECTANGLES

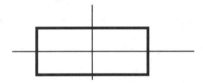

Rectangles have two lines of symmetry.

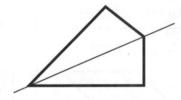

This is what you get if you try to reflect them diagonally! (a kite)

PARALLELOGRAMS

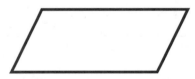

Parallelograms do not have **any** lines of symmetry.

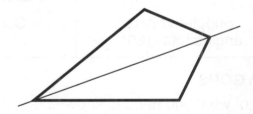

This is what you get if you try to reflect them diagonally. (Oh no! It's a kite again!)

The second sign has rotation symmetry (see next page) but not reflection symmetry

MATHSFACT
The human body, like that of most other animals, has one mirror line right down the middle. However, if you look closely, you will see that it is never quite exact: One eye is a bit bigger than the other, one ear is slightly lower than the other and so on. Your reflection is not the *you* that other people see!

● You need to understand rotation symmetry in two-dimensional shapes.

If you can picture in your mind how many right-ways up a picture has, then you know its order of rotational symmetry. Don't worry if you find this difficult to do in your head. It's a very good idea to trace the shape and then turn the tracing paper round to see if the tracing will fit over the original as it turns.

13+

ORDER OF ROTATION

If a shape has *rotation symmetry order 2*, then it simply means that the shape looks the same in two positions as it is turned around. *Order 3* means it looks the same in three positions and so on.

order 2

order 3

order 4

CENTRE OF ROTATION

The *centre of rotation* is the name given to the point on a picture where you would put a pin if you wanted to spin it round. See if you can find the centre of rotation for each of the three pictures above.

What is the smallest number of squares you have to shade in order to give the pattern rotation symmetry of order 4?

5 more squares

MATHSFACT

Clockwise or anticlockwise? The hair at the crown of your head grows out either clockwise or anticlockwise, the direction usually being inherited. Which way do you grow?

13+

- You need to be able to draw 3-D objects in 2-D, using isometric paper.

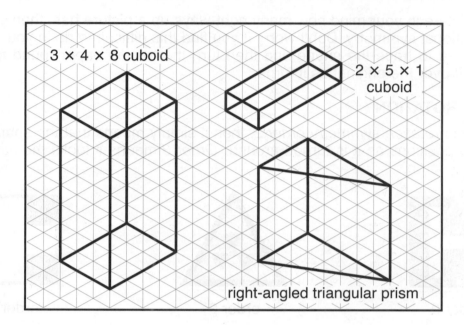

3 × 4 × 8 cuboid

2 × 5 × 1 cuboid

right-angled triangular prism

Tips

1. Hold the paper the right way up. You need straight vertical lines, not straight horizontal lines.

2. Use the lines on the paper to guide your drawing.

3. Look at the way right angles are drawn – they are not 90 degrees!

4. Use your ruler carefully. Check especially that you are drawing parallel lines of equal length on corresponding edges.

S

MATHSFACT

We live in a 3-dimensional world, but mathematicians often work with any number of dimensions, even as many as 99! Edwin Abbot, a London clergyman, wrote a little book in 1884 called *Flatland* about an adventure in a purely two-dimensional world. 2-D or not 2-D, that is the question . . .

QUADRILATERAL THINKING

● You need to know the types and properties of the different quadrilaterals.

diagram of shape	lines of symmetry	order of rotation	notes
square	4	4	The only regular quadrilateral: four equal sides and four equal angles. Diagonals bisect each other at right angles.
rectangle	2	2	Includes squares (that is, a square is a special type of rectangle). Non-square ones are called 'oblongs'. Diagonals bisect each other.
rhombus	2	2	Diamond – includes squares. Opposite angles are equal. Diagonals bisect each other at right angles.
parallelogram	0	2	Includes rhombus, rectangle and square. Opposite angles are equal. Diagonals bisect each other.
arrow head	1	1	The only concave quadrilateral: one diagonal is external. A special type of kite. Diagonals do not intersect.
kite	1	1	Includes rhombus, square and arrowhead. One pair of opposite equal angles. Diagonals intersect at right angles.
(isosceles) trapezium	1 or 0	1	Includes rectangle, parallelogram, and square. The isosceles trapezium has two equal sides and two equal angles.

13+

S

MATHSFACT
It is impossible to find a quadrilateral which will not tessellate.

57

SIR CUMFERENCE AND THE AREA OF THE ROUND TABLE

> ● You need to know the formulae for circles, and apply them to circumference, area and volume calculations.

Start by reminding yourself of the words used to describe the parts of a circle on page 92.

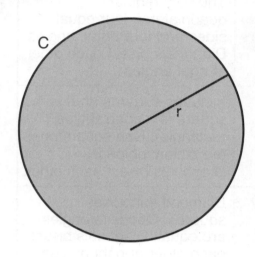

abbreviations	meaning
r	radius
d	diameter
C	circumference
A	area
h	height (of a cylinder, for example)

(Note that we use capital letters for C and A.)

You need to learn these formulae:

$$d = 2r$$
$$C = \pi d$$
$$C = 2\pi r$$
$$A = \pi r^2$$
$$\text{volume of cylinder} = \pi r^2 h$$

If there is no π (pi) on your calculator, then you can use 3.14 instead. A more accurate value of pi is on page 92!

Example

How far along the ground will a wheel of radius 30 cm travel if it turns 1000 times?

The radius is 30 cm (0.3 m).

So the circumference (one turn of the wheel) is 2 × π × 0.3 which comes to 1.88496 m.

Thus after 1000 turns, the wheel has travelled 1884.96 m or about 1.9 km.

MATHSFACT

There has been a new Pi Memorisation Record in UK prep schools. Matthew from Highfield School held it for several years with 200 places, but has now been beaten by Kristian from Elstree with 300 places (Oct 2005). Both boys were in Year seven at the time. Kristian also holds the record for the fastest recitation of the first 100 digits with a personal best of 16.29 seconds. Could you beat them?

ENLARGEMENT

- You need to understand the importance of *scale factor* and *centre of enlargement* when making enlargement constructions.

CONSTRUCTING AN ENLARGEMENT

Step 1. Draw a line from the centre of enlargement to each corner of the shape **and keep going**.

Step 2. For each corner of the shape, measure the distance from the centre of enlargement and multiply this by the scale factor. Mark a new point along the same line of this new distance from the centre of enlargement.

Step 3. Join up all the points made in Step 2.

Example

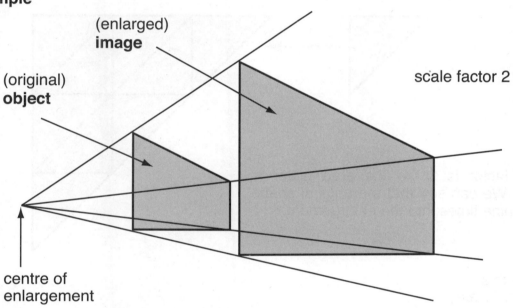

(enlarged)
image

(original)
object

scale factor 2

centre of
enlargement

When one shape is an enlargement of the other we call them *similar*.

FINDING THE CENTRE OF ENLARGEMENT AND THE SCALE FACTOR

If the construction has already been made, draw lines from each corner of the image to its corresponding corner on the object **and keep going**. The point where these lines intersect is the centre of enlargement. To find the scale factor, just choose any two corresponding edges: the scale factor is the length of the image edge divided by the length of the object edge.

S

MATHSFACT

The earliest known example of a book on Applied Mathematics was one on surveying by Richard de Benese: his 'Boke of Measuring of Lande' was published between 1562 and 1575.

● You need to understand the importance of the area factor when making enlargement constructions.

13+

Recall from page 59 that the scale factor was the number by which all lengths were multiplied to make the enlargement (so a scale factor of 2 produced a ×2 enlargement).

Area factor is similar. It is the number by which the original area is multiplied to obtain the area of the enlargement. The clever part of it is that there is an easy link between the two.

> To find the area factor you just square the scale factor.

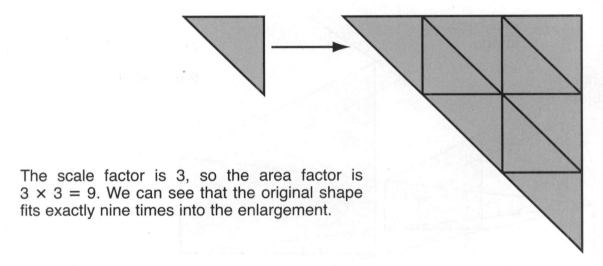

The scale factor is 3, so the area factor is 3 × 3 = 9. We can see that the original shape fits exactly nine times into the enlargement.

similarly for this enlargement (scale factor 2)

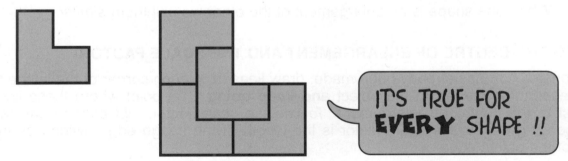

IT'S TRUE FOR **EVERY** SHAPE !!

S

MATHSFACT

Area Factor is Scale Factor squared; Volume Factor is Scale Factor cubed. Therefore if you double the measurements of a box, you will need 4 times as much cardboard but it will hold 8 times as much stuff!

THE CALCULATION AREA

● You need to be able to calculate the area of any shape, including fractional and composite ones.

FRACTIONAL AND COMPOSITE SHAPES

Fractional shapes are those which are ordinary shapes such as rectangles and circles, but with holes cut out or pieces missing. You calculate the area of a fractional shape using subtraction.

Composite shapes are those which are made by sticking together simpler shapes such as squares and triangles. You calculate the area of a composite shape using addition.

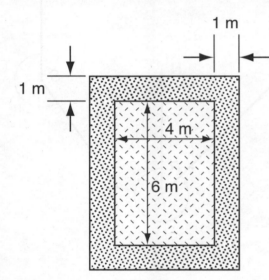

The path round this small garden is 1 m wide. The area of the path is found by subtracting the area of the garden from the area of the surrounding rectangle.

area of garden = 4 × 6
= 24 m^2

area of surrounding rectangle =

(1 + 4 + 1) × (1 + 6 + 1) = 48 m^2

so area of path = 48 − 24
= 24 m^2

With composite shapes, it is usually up to you to work out the best way of dividing the area up into simpler shapes.

Of course, it doesn't actually matter which way you do it – they all give the same answer!

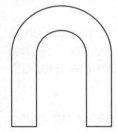

This archway looks complicated but it is really just made up of simpler shapes, as the second diagram clearly shows.

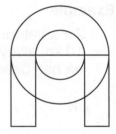

When working out its area, we would subtract the area of the small circle from the area of the large circle and then halve the answer to find the area of the curved part of the arch. To this we would add the area of the two rectangular feet and obtain the final answer.

S

MATHSFACT

From the top of the highest mountain to the bottom of the deepest sea trench is only about 20 km. This thin 'life zone' is just 0.3% of the Earth's diameter, equivalent to a coat of varnish on a snooker ball.

TEDDY BEARINGS

● You need to be able to use 3-figure bearings in measuring and constructions.

Examples

13+

Try these! *(You'll have to check your answers with your maths teacher.)* In each case find the bearing from *P, Q, R* or *S*.

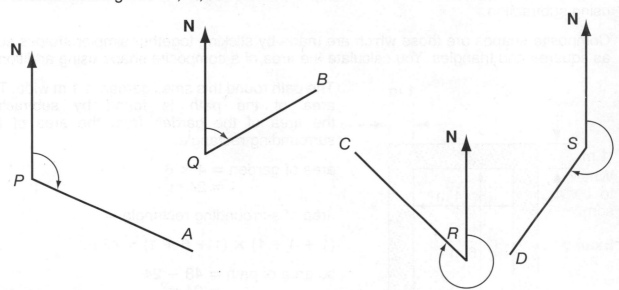

GENERAL ADVICE

● Always measure **clockwise** from **north**.
● Try to measure to the nearest degree.
● Make sure you have read the direction the right way round. *The bearing of X from Y* means put a north line through *Y*, then measure round as far as the line joining *Y* to *X*.

Example

An amateur pilot leaves the airfield in his plane and flies towards an island which is 10 km away on a bearing of 095°. However, after he has flown 10 km, he notices that he has been flying on a bearing of 085° by mistake. How far is he from the island?

scale 1 cm : 1 km

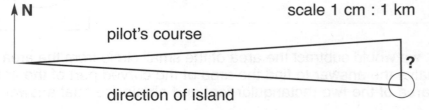

Careful measuring gives the length of the line as 1.7 cm, and so the pilot is 1.7 km or 1700 m off course!

MATHSFACT

The UK leads the way in music purchases. Every year, an average of 2.9 albums are bought by every man, woman and child in the country. Norway is next (2.7), closely followed by USA (2.6).

IN CONCLUSION

> ● You need to be able to draw valid conclusions from a variety of graphs, charts and diagrams.

Whatever the type of graph, it is important to look at the whole picture before you try to conclude anything. Many graphs are deliberately misleading because they have something to hide – the newspapers are full of examples – don't be deceived!

Example

Which country below has more rain?

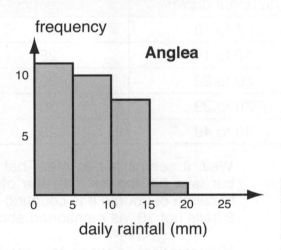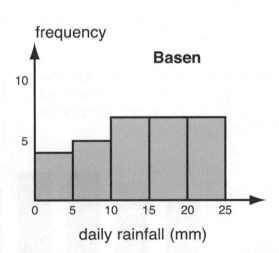

At a first quick glance, you might be forgiven for thinking that it was Anglea because of its tall bars. However, it is in fact Basen, because it has fewer days of low rain (0–5 mm) and more days of high rain (20–25 mm) than Anglea.

> **MATHSFACT**
>
> The apparently simple game of noughts and crosses can end after 5, 6, 7, 8 or 9 plays. There are 255 168 possible games. Playing completely at random, the probability that the first player will win is 58.5%.

BAA-BAA BAR CHART

(See also pages 22 and 63.)

13+

Example

The first 20 draws of the UK National Lottery produced these numbers (7 each week) in the order given. Bonus numbers are printed in **bold type**.

30	3	5	44	14	22	**10**	16	6	44	31	12
15	**37**	21	11	17	30	29	40	**31**	26	47	49
43	35	38	**28**	13	3	38	5	14	9	**30**	27
29	39	3	44	2	**6**	17	44	36	32	9	42
16	21	32	2	5	25	22	**46**	23	38	17	7
32	42	**48**	47	6	16	31	30	20	**4**	31	16
25	43	4	26	**21**	46	42	1	38	7	37	**20**
48	38	15	29	18	35	**5**	45	16	36	19	21
29	**43**	18	33	8	31	5	10	**28**	17	36	11
12	42	26	**13**	2	22	13	46	29	27	**36**	41
19	31	18	9	24	**21**	4	49	41	44	42	17
24	43	41	22	25	30	32	**29**				

To make a frequency chart of these numbers, we first draw up a frequency table.

Note that we have had to make the first group (1 to 9), only 9 numbers instead of 10, because there is no zero ball.

numbers drawn	frequency
1 to 9	24
10 to 19	28
20 to 29	30
30 to 39	30
40 to 49	28

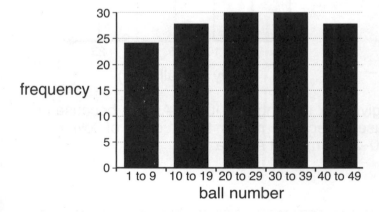

Well, it seems fair to me. That first bar is a bit shorter than the others because of course it is counting only 9 balls not 10, as mentioned above.

Mathematical pause for thought: every time somebody becomes a lottery millionaire, it means that between them the others have lost over a million pounds.

D

AS EASY AS PIE

● You need to be able to construct and interpret simple pie charts, using degrees or percentages.

13+

Example

Twenty children were asked about their favourite ice cream. The replies were as follows:

chocolate: 9, vanilla: 6, strawberry: 4, toffee: 1; total: 20

Display the results of the ice cream survey using a pie chart.

For a pie chart measured in degrees, this total of 20 must be made into 360°. For a pie chart measured in percentages, it must be made into 100%. We shall work through both calculations here.

DEGREES VERSION 360° ÷ 20 = 18°, so each child is represented by 18°.

flavour	frequency	factor		angle of sector
chocolate	9	× 18°	=	162°
vanilla	6	× 18°	=	108°
strawberry	4	× 18°	=	72°
toffee	1	× 18°	=	18°
total	20		total	360°

PERCENTAGE VERSION 100% ÷ 20 = 5%, so each child is represented by 5%.

flavour	frequency	factor		angle of sector
chocolate	9	× 5%	=	45%
vanilla	6	× 5%	=	30%
strawberry	4	× 5%	=	20%
toffee	1	× 5%	=	5%
total	20		total	100%

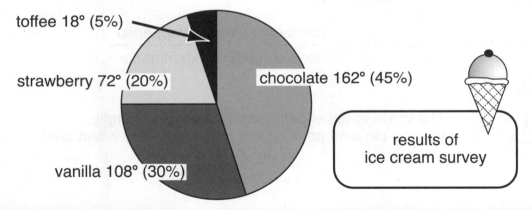

toffee 18° (5%)

strawberry 72° (20%)

chocolate 162° (45%)

vanilla 108° (30%)

results of ice cream survey

D

MATHSFACT

Take any long strip of paper and carefully tie an ordinary knot in it. You will find that if you pull it just tight enough you can flatten it neatly. Now hold the paper up to the light to see a regular pentagon in the knot.

PROBABILITY ABILITY

- You need to be familiar with the probability scale from 0 to 1 and know the difference between experimental and theoretical probabilities.

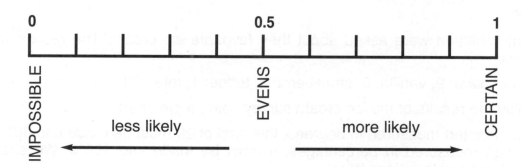

THEORETICAL PROBABILITY

This is calculated using a simple fraction:

$$\text{probability of } \mathbf{A} \text{ happening} = \frac{\text{number of ways } \mathbf{A} \text{ can happen}}{\text{total number of equally likely possibilities}}$$

Example

What is the probability of rolling an even number with an ordinary die with six faces?

It can happen in three ways (2, 4 or 6).

There are six equally likely possibilities in total (1, 2, 3, 4, 5 and 6).

So the probability of rolling an even number is $\frac{3}{6}$, or 0.5 (50%).

EXPERIMENTAL PROBABILITY

This is calculated using a similar fraction:

$$\text{probability of } \mathbf{X} \text{ happening} = \frac{\text{number of times } \mathbf{X} \text{ happened}}{\text{total number of experiments}}$$

Example

The drawing-pin experiment is a familiar example.
Will the pin land point up or on one side? Try it and see!

D

MATHSFACT

You are seven times more likely to be struck by lightning than win the Lottery.

A PROBABILITY SUM

> ● You need to know that the sum of all probabilities in a situation is one.

13+

First of all, why is the sum of all probabilities in a situation one? Well, it goes back to page 66 where we saw that *certainty* had a probability of 1

When we say that the sum of all probabilities is 1, all we are saying in effect is that it is certain that **something** will happen. Quite obvious really!

Let's see now how useful that fact can be.

Example 1

The probability that Tom will be picked for the school hockey team is 0.7

What is the probability that he won't be picked?

The total probability (will + won't) is 1

The probability that he will be picked is 0.7

So the probability that he won't is (1 − 0.7) **0.3**

Example 2

When I 'phone my friend Anne, the probability that she will answer is 0.3 and the probability that someone else in her family will answer is 0.4

The probability that no one answers is 0.1; the only other possibility is that the line is engaged. What is the probability that the line is engaged?

The sum of all these probabilities is 0.8

So the probability that the line is engaged is **0.2**

D

> **MATHSFACT**
>
> If you want to gain a reputation as an accurate weather forecaster, simply give the weather tomorrow always as 'the same as today'.

● You need to be able to list systematically all possible outcomes of an experiment.

13+

Examples

1. How many different 4-digit numbers can you make using 7, 3, 1 and 4 once only?

Well, there's 7314 and 3741 and 1743 and ....

It would be difficult to carry on like this without missing numbers out or repeating earlier ones. Being systematic means being organised in your approach. Like this, for example:

1347	1374	1437	1473	1734	1743
3147	3174	3417	3471	3714	3741
4137	4173	4317	4371	4713	4731
7134	7143	7314	7341	7413	7431

If you got a **MESSY ATTIC** from the **MYSTIC EAST** then get **SYSTEMATIC!**

Read across the rows above. Can you see my method?

I can be certain now that there are no numbers missing, because there is nowhere in my system that would let them in!

2. The table on the right shows all the possible outcomes when two dice are rolled and the scores added together. It then becomes very easy to see that a total of 7 can be reached in six different ways, making it the most likely total, but 2 and 12 can only be made in one way, making them the two least likely totals.

+	1	2	3	4	5	6
1	2	3	4	5	6	7
2	3	4	5	6	7	8
3	4	5	6	7	8	9
4	5	6	7	8	9	10
5	6	7	8	9	10	11
6	7	8	9	10	11	12

3. What are the possible outcomes when three coins are tossed onto a desk at the same time?

possibility	1	2	3	4	5	6	7	8
coin 1	H	H	H	H	T	T	T	T
coin 2	H	H	T	T	H	H	T	T
coin 3	H	T	H	T	H	T	H	T

Once again, careful listing shows all eight possibilities very clearly. What patterns can you find in the way the letters **H** and **T** have been written in the table?

D

MATHSFACT

A famous problem called the *Four Colour Problem* was eventually solved by two mathematicians in 1976, by getting a computer to list all possible outcomes. It was certainly a systematic solution. The list unfortunately went on over hundreds of pages!

● You need to be able to construct and interpret scattergraphs and correlation diagrams.

Sometimes the data we collect comes in pairs of numbers. We might ask people for their height and mass, for example, or we might measure oxygen levels at different altitudes. To keep each data item as a pair, we plot them as Cartesian (x, y) co-ordinates:

(x, y) = (height, mass) or

(x, y) = (altitude, oxygen level) and so on.

When we have plotted several points, we end up with a graph called a *scattergraph*.

13+

Examples

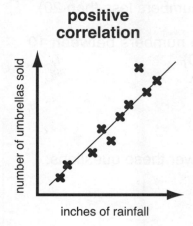

positive correlation

number of umbrellas sold

inches of rainfall

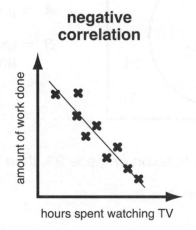

negative correlation

amount of work done

hours spent watching TV

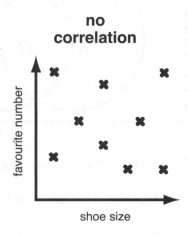

no correlation

favourite number

shoe size

Note that when there is either positive or negative correlation, we can draw a line showing the approximate direction of the trend in the points.

This line, drawn by eye, is called the *line of best fit*.

When there is correlation (positive or negative), it means that the pairs of numbers are related in some way.

MATHSFACT

In 1582 Gregory XIII decided to correct the highly inaccurate calendar by removing 11 days. People went to bed in the evening of October 3rd, and when they woke up the following morning they found it was October 15th! The change was adopted in England in September 1752.

D

GAME, SET AND VENN DIAGRAM

- You need to be able to understand set notation and construct and interpret Venn diagrams.

Sets are simply collections of things, all of which have something in common. For example, we might talk about the set of odd numbers less than 20, or the set of prime numbers between 10 and 30

With Venn diagrams we can show things which are in more than one set at the same time.

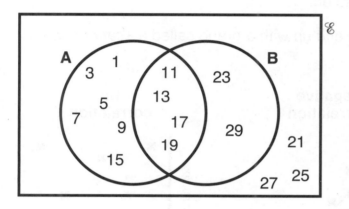

$\mathscr{E}$ = {odd numbers less than 30}

A = {odd numbers less than 20}

B = {prime numbers between 10 and 30}

Remind yourself of the special notation on page 93, then answer these questions.

1. List the members of the set $A \cap B$.

2. Find $n(A')$.

3. How would you describe numbers in the set $(A \cup B)'$?

MATHSFACT

John Venn, the English mathematician behind these diagrams, was born in 1834 in Hull. As a mathematician he specialised in *Logic* and *Probability*, and he used these circles to prove his logical arguments.

QUADRATIC TRIAL AND IMPROVEMENT

- You need to be able to solve quadratic equations using trial and improvement methods.

A *root* of an equation is a value of x which will make the value of that equation equal to zero. Quadratic equations can have two different roots.

Trial and improvement helps you to zoom in on one of those roots. You are usually told where to start looking and then each subsequent trial improves your answer.

Example

The equation $x^2 - 3x + 1 = 0$ has a root (solution) between $x = 2$ and $x = 3$

Find this value of x to 2 decimal places.

x	$x^2 - 3x + 1$	verdict
2	−1	too small
3	1	too big
2.5	−0.25	too small
2.7	0.19	too big
2.6	−0.04	too small
2.65	0.0725	too big
2.62	0.0044	too big
2.61	−0.0179	too small
2.615	−0.006775	too small

We always choose our next x value to be half way between the most recent *too small* and *too big* values.

Our conclusion at this stage is that x must be between 2.615 and 2.62, both of which are 2.62 to two decimal places.

In order to give an answer to two decimal places, we must calculate to three decimal places.

If x is between two numbers which both round to 2.62 to two decimal places, then x must also round to 2.62 to two decimal places.

It's been trapped! *(See MATHSFACT below.)*

MATHSFACT

'Algebra is a merry science,' Uncle Jakob would say. 'We go hunting for a little animal whose name we don't know, so we call it x. When we bag our game, we pounce on it and give it its right name.' (Albert Einstein)

> ● You need to be able to describe algebraically the *n*th term of a sequence where the rule is linear.

This follows on very simply and neatly from the work on the previous page. We just need to learn a bit of special notation for sequences.

13+
E

n   The number of the term indicates the **position** in the sequence: $n = 1$ for the first term in the sequence, $n = 2$ for the second term and so on.

T_n As for the *n*th term itself, **T** stands for *term*, and ***n*** can be any number *(see above)*. Thus we have T_1 for the first term, T_2 for the second term and so on.

Example

Find the *n*th term of the sequence   2, 7, 12, 17, ...

We start by making a table:

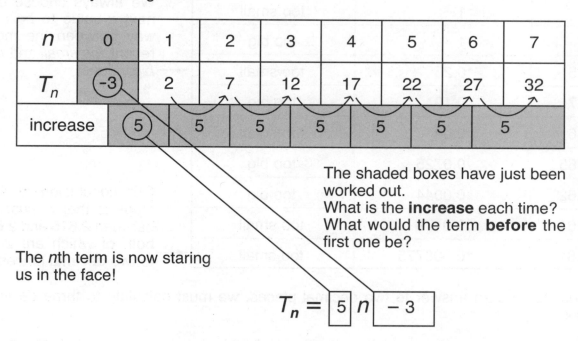

n	0	1	2	3	4	5	6	7
T_n	-3	2	7	12	17	22	27	32
increase	5	5	5	5	5	5	5	

The shaded boxes have just been worked out.
What is the **increase** each time?
What would the term **before** the first one be?

The *n*th term is now staring us in the face!

$$T_n = \boxed{5}\, n \;\boxed{-3}$$

N/A

> **MATHSFACT**
>
> According to C F Gauss, 'Mathematics is the Queen of the Sciences, and the Theory of Numbers is the Queen of Mathematics.' Other writers additionally believe that algebra is 'the jewel in her crown'.

QUADRATIC RULES OK

> ● You need to be familiar with nth terms and substitution into a quadratic rule.

Example

Can you find the next two terms of this sequence: 4, 7, 12, 19, 28, ...?

We can make a table similar to the one on page 72:

n	1	2	3	4	5	6	7
T_n	4	7	12	19	28	39	52
increase		3	5	7	9	11	13
increase			2	2	2	2	2

As you can see, for quadratic rules we need **two** rows of differences in the table. It turns out (you wouldn't be expected to find it for yourself at Common Entrance or Key Stage 3) that the quadratic rule for the above sequence is

$$T_n = n^2 + 3$$

It is much easier if you are told the rule at the start. To find each term, you just substitute $n = 1, 2, 3, ...$ into the formula.

Example

Give the first three terms of the sequence $T_n = 2n^2 - 1$

Substituting in $n = 1$, we obtain $2 \times 1 - 1 = 1$
$\qquad\qquad\quad n = 2$, $\qquad\qquad 2 \times 4 - 1 = 7$
$\qquad\qquad\quad n = 3$, $\qquad\qquad 2 \times 9 - 1 = 17$

So the first three terms are 1, 7 and 17.

MATHSFACT

The word *quadratic* means *square*. In ancient Greece, Euclid and his fellow mathematicians didn't square numbers as we do, but tended to speak of numbers as lengths, and squares as areas.

SIMULTANEOUS EQUATIONS

● You need to be able to solve simultaneous equations graphically and algebraically.

Any pair of simultaneous equations may be solved using algebra or by drawing a graph. Consider the following pair of simultaneous equations:

$$2x - 3y = 4 \quad ①$$
$$3x + 2y = 19 \quad ②$$

These equations will be solved both ways to show and compare the two methods.

ALGEBRAIC METHOD

We note that equations ① and ② have opposite signs in the middle. We will therefore want to add them. (If the signs were the same, then we would subtract.) To do this, first make the y coefficients the same:

① × 2 is $\qquad 4x - 6y = 8 \quad ③$

② × 3 is $\qquad 9x + 6y = 57 \quad ④$

Add ③ and ④ $\quad 13x = 65$

$$x = 5$$

Substitute $x = 5$ into ②:

$$15 + 2y = 19$$
$$2y = 4$$
$$y = 2$$

Check

① $10 - 6 = 4$ OK!

② $15 + 4 = 19$ OK!

GRAPHICAL METHOD

We make a table for each equation so that we can draw them both as straight line graphs.

① becomes $3y = 2x - 4$

x	2	5	8
$2x - 4$	0	6	12
y	0	2	4

② becomes $2y = 19 - 3x$

x	1	3	5
$19 - 3x$	16	10	4
y	8	5	2

which we then plot and draw, as has been done below.

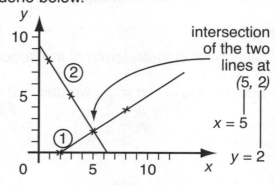

intersection of the two lines at (5, 2)

$x = 5$

$y = 2$

Thus we are able to read off from the graph that the solution to our simultaneous equations is $x = 5$, $y = 2$

MATHSFACT

If there are two unknowns, you need two equations to find them. Three unknowns need three equations and so on. C F Gauss (1777–1855) developed a clever way of solving the most complicated examples.

SOME ARE MORE EQUAL THAN OTHERS

● You need to be able to solve simple inequalities and find integer solution sets.

INEQUALITIES

Example

Consider the inequality: $5 + \frac{1}{2}x > 4$

Subtract 5 from both sides. $\frac{1}{2}x > {}^-1$

Multiply by 2 $x > {}^-2$

So x could be $^-1$, 0, 1, 2, 3, 4, 5, ...

Any of these would make $\left(5 + \frac{1}{2}x\right)$ more than 4

We could show the solution on a number line, by shading out the part that we don't want:

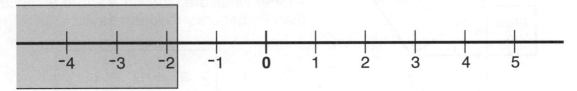

Suppose further that: $2x - 5 < 1$
Add 5 to both sides $2x < 6$
Divide through by 2 $x < 3$
Represented on the number line as:

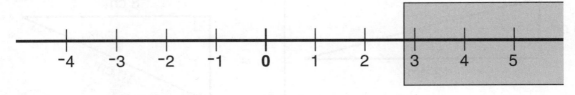

Then the set of integers which satisfies both inequalities at the same time (the integer solution set) is shown by the combination diagram below:

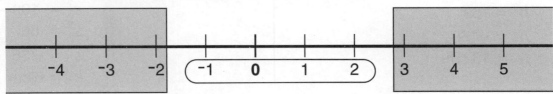

MATHSFACT

It is impossible to place 75 eggs into 13 baskets so that each basket contains a different number of eggs.

PYTHAGORAS THE GREAT

● You need to know and apply Pythagoras' theorem in two dimensions.

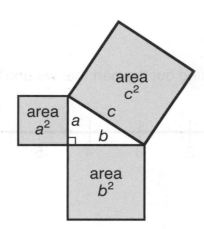

'The square on the hypotenuse is equal to the sum of the squares on the other two sides.'

If the hypotenuse is labelled c and the two shorter sides are labelled a and b respectively, then Pythagoras' theorem says:

$$a^2 + b^2 = c^2$$

FINDING THE HYPOTENUSE

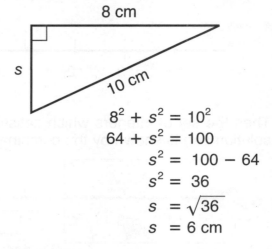

$h^2 = 5^2 + 12^2$
$h^2 = 25 + 144$
$h^2 = 169$
$h = \sqrt{169}$
$h = 13$ cm

FINDING A SHORT SIDE

$8^2 + s^2 = 10^2$
$64 + s^2 = 100$
$s^2 = 100 - 64$
$s^2 = 36$
$s = \sqrt{36}$
$s = 6$ cm

MATHSFACT

Pythagoras' Theorem first appeared around 300 BC in Book 1 of Euclid's *Elements (Proposition 47)*. Tradition holds that Pythagoras sacrificed an ox in honour of his discovery, but many claim that it was known long before him!

PUMP UP THE VOLUME

> ● You need to be able to calculate the volume of any solid, including prisms.

Check that you are familiar with the standard volume formulae on page 91, especially of the prism. We have already met the volume of a cylinder or circular prism *(page 58)*, so here are two more:

sphere volume $= \frac{4}{3} \pi r^3$

volume of pyramid (including cone) $= \frac{1}{3} \times$ base area $\times$ height

Example 1

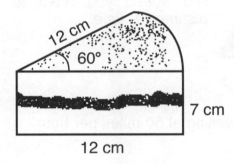

A cake in the shape of a cylinder (height 7 cm, radius 12 cm) is cut into sectors of 60 degrees each. Find the volume of each piece.

$360° \div 60° = 6$, so each piece is $\frac{1}{6}$ of the cake.

volume of whole cake (cylinder) $= \pi r^2 h$

so volume of cake is $\pi \times 12^2 \times 7 = 3166.725$ cm^3

thus volume of piece $= 527.8$ cm^3

Example 2

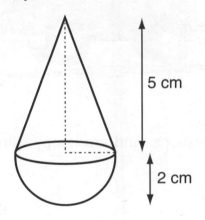

The base of this toy is a hemisphere (half a sphere).

To find the volume of the toy we add up the volumes of the upper cone and the lower hemisphere:

volume of hemisphere $= \frac{1}{2} \times \frac{4}{3} \times \pi \times 2^3$

$= 16.76$ cm^3

volume of cone $= \frac{1}{3} \times (\pi \times 2^2) \times 5$

$= 20.94$ cm^3

so volume of toy $= 37.7$ cm^3

MATHSFACT

A four-dimensional hyper-pyramid has a volume equal to one quarter of its base volume multiplied by its height in the fourth direction. As with all 4-D shapes, the hyperpyramid has a 3-D shadow.

TRAVEL AGENT

● You need to be able to solve problems involving distance, speed and time calculations.

If you learn the 'magic triangle' below, then you will surely become a wizard at working out these problems!

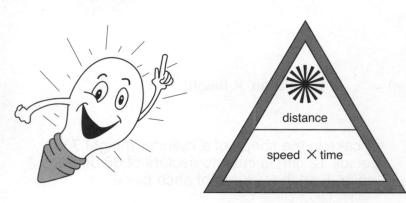

HOW IT WORKS

Simply put your finger over the one you want to find and the magic triangle tells you what calculation to do with the other two. For example, to find *speed* you have to do *distance ÷ time*.

**13+
E**

SIMPLE SAMPLE QUESTION

How long does it take to travel 80 miles if you are travelling at 50 miles per hour?

time = distance ÷ speed
= 80 ÷ 50
= 1.6 hours

(OK, but what does the 0.6 hours mean?)

0.6 hours = 0.6 × 60 minutes
= 36 minutes

So the journey takes 1 hour 36 minutes.

Note

If you have your own step-by-step method for these questions, and are happy with it, stick with it! Any method which works is fine.

S

MATHSFACT

Sound waves travel at 1224 km per hour. Light waves travel at 300 000 km per second and nothing can possibly travel faster. A light year is not a length of time, but a distance – the distance travelled by light in one year.

> ● One popular extension topic is Trigonometry, which is just about lengths and angles in triangles.

You've already met Mr Pythagoras on page 76, and he helped us out whenever we wanted to find the length of one side of a right-angled triangle when we knew the other two sides.

This page is about sine, cosine and tangent, and those funny buttons on your calculator which look like this: [sin] [cos] [tan] (obviously these are just abbreviations).

Above these buttons you will usually see $\sin^{-1}$, $\cos^{-1}$ and $\tan^{-1}$, and these just do the opposite or inverse function. You also need to check your calculator shows **d** or **deg** and not **r** (**radians**) or **g** (**grads**) so that it works out the angles in degrees. *(See your maths teacher if you need to change this – it usually involves pressing MODE or something.)*

13+ E

TRIANGLE ANATOMY

You need to learn the special names of the parts of the triangle.

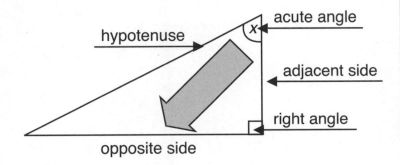

acute angle

hypotenuse

adjacent side

right angle

opposite side

> The Hypotenuse (Hyp) is always the longest side, and always opposite the right angle.
> The Opposite side (Opp) is always opposite the acute angle you are studying (imagine a torch shining on the OPPOSITE wall).
> The Adjacent side (Adj) is always between the acute angle and the right angle, adjacent to (next to) the acute angle.

FINDING AN ANGLE

Use the two sides you are given in the above diagram, divide one by the other as shown below and then use the appropriate inverse function to find the angle.

Sin (x) = OPP ÷ HYP   Cos (x) = ADJ ÷ HYP   Tan (x) = OPP ÷ ADJ

(You can remember this by saying 'SOHCAHTOA' !!)

FINDING A SIDE

Label your triangle as above, based on the angle you are given. You only need to know one other side. Then use SOHCAHTOA again to find the missing side.

For example, if you are given an angle of 42° and a hypotenuse of 12 cm, and you have to find the adjacent, then you need Cos since this is the only one with Adj and Hyp.

Write Cos (42°) = ? ÷ 12 and find the Adj by working out 12 × Cos (42°) = 8.92 cm.

S

> **MATHSFACT**
> The librarians in Rome would have had to create a new classification in 1464 in order to file a copy of Regiomontanus' new book, *De triangulis omnimodis libri V – Trigonometry*.

13+
E

MATHSFACT
Write down the number 1 and follow it with 80 zeros. You have just written down a number which is bigger than the total number of sub-atomic particles in the entire known universe. Now try counting up to it.

11+

THE MULTIPLICATION TABLE

X	1	2	3	4	5	6	7	8	9	10	11	12
1	1	2	3	4	5	6	7	8	9	10	11	12
2	2	4	6	8	10	12	14	16	18	20	22	24
3	3	6	9	12	15	18	21	24	27	30	33	36
4	4	8	12	16	20	24	28	32	36	40	44	48
5	5	10	15	20	25	30	35	40	45	50	55	60
6	6	12	18	24	30	36	42	48	54	60	66	72
7	7	14	21	28	35	42	49	56	63	70	77	84
8	8	16	24	32	40	48	56	64	72	80	88	96
9	9	18	27	36	45	54	63	72	81	90	99	108
10	10	20	30	40	50	60	70	80	90	100	110	120
11	11	22	33	44	55	66	77	88	99	110	121	132
12	12	24	36	48	60	72	84	96	108	120	132	144

You need to know your tables in several ways. First of all, learn them in columns so that you can list, for example, all multiples of seven. Then, be able to jump in at any point, and know that, e.g. 4 × 8 = 32, without thinking. Finally, you should be able to use it backwards and be able to give all factor pairs of a number (e.g. which numbers multiply to give thirty-six?).

R

THE FIRST 100 PRIME NUMBERS

2	3	5	7	11	13	17	19	23	29
31	37	41	43	47	53	59	61	67	71
73	79	83	89	97	101	103	107	109	113
127	131	137	139	149	151	157	163	167	173
179	181	191	193	197	199	211	223	227	229
233	239	241	251	257	263	269	271	277	281
283	293	307	311	313	317	331	337	347	349
353	359	367	373	379	383	389	397	401	409
419	421	431	433	439	443	449	457	461	463
467	479	487	491	499	503	509	521	523	541

N/A

Obviously you do not need to learn all these! Try to be familiar with as many as you can, though. At the very least learn the first ten or so, and reach the point where you can recognise all numbers under 100 as either prime or not.

> **MATHSFACT**
> The largest prime so far discovered (Sep 2006) is one with 9 808 358 digits. It is the 44th Mersenne Prime: $2^{32\,582\,657} - 1$ and was found as part of the Great Internet Mersenne Prime Search. See www.mersenne.org for more!

SQUARES, CUBES AND ROOTS

Multiply any number by itself and the result is a square number. Any number multiplied by its square gives a cube number. It is an extremely good idea to know the squares of at least the first ten numbers and at least the first five cubes. Here are the first fifteen of each:

n	n^2	n^3
1	1	1
2	4	8
3	9	27
4	16	64
5	25	125
6	36	216
7	49	343
8	64	512
9	81	729
10	100	1000
11	121	1331
12	144	1728
13	169	2197
14	196	2744
15	225	3375

n^2 means n to the power of 2

2 is the index number

similarly, for n^3 3 is the index number

Remember the connection between squares and square roots.

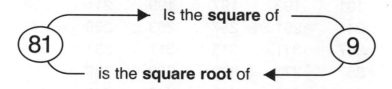

Cubes and cube roots work in a similar way.

MATHSFACT

639172 is the largest number with distinct digits whose square (408540845584) contains none of those digits.

THE 24-HOUR CLOCK; THE NUMBER LINE

THE 24-HOUR CLOCK

Note that all you have to do is add 12 to the normal numbers on the clock to find the 24-hr clock equivalents.

Use am (morning) and pm (afternoon) only when using the 12-hr clock.

When using the 24-hr clock always write the time using four digits.

The time shown on this clock depends on whether it is morning or afternoon.

morning   1.55 am (12-hr clock)   01.55 (24-hr clock)

afternoon   1.55 pm (12-hr clock)   13.55 (24-hr clock)

THE NUMBER LINE

A number line, either drawn on paper or imagined, is often the best way to help you add or subtract with negative numbers. Here are four number lines using different scales:

```
-7  -6  -5  -4  -3  -2  -1   0   1   2   3   4   5   6   7   8
 |   |   |   |   |   |   |   |   |   |   |   |   |   |   |   |

-14 -12 -10 -8  -6  -4  -2   0   2   4   6   8  10  12  14  16
 |   |   |   |   |   |   |   |   |   |   |   |   |   |   |   |

-35 -30 -25 -20 -15 -10  -5   0   5  10  15  20  25  30  35  40
 |   |   |   |   |   |   |   |   |   |   |   |   |   |   |   |

-70 -60 -50 -40 -30 -20 -10   0  10  20  30  40  50  60  70  80
 |   |   |   |   |   |   |   |   |   |   |   |   |   |   |   |
```

MATHSFACT
A stopped clock shows the correct time more often than one which is five minutes slow.

11+

ODD AND EVEN NUMBER RULES

There are several general rules about combining two numbers, depending on whether they are odd or even. You may wish to think about why these rules always work as they do.

odd + odd = even	odd − odd = even
odd + even = odd	odd − even = odd
even + odd = odd	even − odd = odd
even + even = even	even − even = even

odd × odd = odd

odd × even = even

even × odd = even

even × even = even

> There are no simple rules for division. Any division could be a fraction which is neither odd nor even.

R

MatheMagic – it's even odder than I thought!

Ask two of your friends to help you with this trick. Let's say you asked Horace and Doris. If you knew Boris, Norris, Maurice, Floris or Jack you could ask them. Give 21 counters to Doris and ask her to give some of them to Horace. Make sure they don't tell you how many each person has. Now ask them to do a short calculation and to tell you the result. Immediately you can tell them both whether they are holding either an even number or an odd number of counters!

Making the maths do the magic

Ask Doris to **double** the number of counters in her hand, and then to **add** to the answer the number of counters that Horace is holding. When she tells you the answer, it will be either an **even** or an **odd** number.

If it is **even**, she holds an **odd** number of counters. Horace holds an **even** number.

If it is **odd**, she holds an **even** number of counters. Horace holds an **odd** number.

N/A

MATHSFACT

The distinction between 'odd' and 'even' goes back to ancient times. Odd numbers were thought to be 'divine', 'heavenly' and 'masculine', while the even numbers were 'human', 'earthly' and 'feminine'!

TYPES OF TRIANGLE AND QUADRILATERAL

Triangles and quadrilaterals are so common that we sort them out into different categories according to their properties.

TRIANGLES

1. **Equilateral** triangles have all the angles the same (each 60°) and all sides equal length.
2. **Isosceles** triangles have two equal angles and two equal sides.
3. **Right-angled** triangles have one angle of 90°.
4. **Scalene** triangles are those which are not included in the above list.

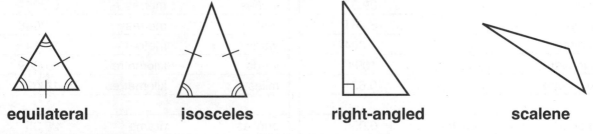

| equilateral | isosceles | right-angled | scalene |

QUADRILATERALS

1. A **square** has four equal sides and four equal angles (each 90°). Opposite sides are parallel.
2. A **rectangle** (oblong) also has four equal (right) angles, but only opposite sides are equal length. Opposite sides are parallel.
3. A **rhombus** (diamond) has four equal sides, but only opposite angles are equal. Opposite sides are parallel.
4. A **parallelogram** has two pairs of parallel sides. Opposite sides are not only parallel but also equal in length. Opposite angles are equal.
5. A **kite** has two pairs of adjacent equal sides and two equal angles.
6. A **trapezium** has one pair of parallel sides. In an isosceles trapezium the non-parallel sides are also equal in length.

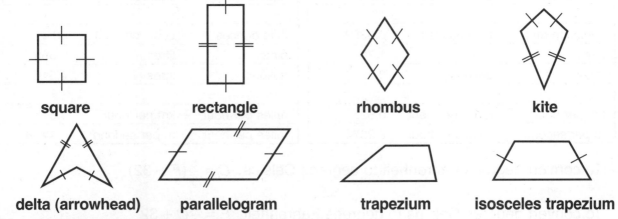

square   rectangle   rhombus   kite

delta (arrowhead)   parallelogram   trapezium   isosceles trapezium

(See page 57 for more quadrilateral properties.)

MATHSFACT

A honeycomb has a hexagonal structure because this is mathematically the best way of packing together lots of individual cells, with no gaps, to give the biggest space and using as little wax as possible.

METRIC AND IMPERIAL UNITS

11+

The system of measurement in use in Britain now is almost completely metric, but many examples of imperial measurements still exist (especially miles, feet, inches, pints, stone and tons), and you should be aware of them.

metric to convert	imperial to	multiply by	imperial to convert	metric to	multiply by
millimetres	inches	0.0394	inches	millimetres	25.4
centimetres	inches	0.3937	inches	centimetres	2.54
centimetres	feet	0.0328	feet	centimetres	30.48
metres	inches	39.37	inches	metres	0.0254
metres	feet	3.281	feet	metres	0.3048
metres	yards	1.094	yards	metres	0.914
kilometres	yards	1094	yards	kilometres	0.0009
kilometres	miles	0.621	miles	kilometres	1.609
grams	ounces	0.035	ounces	grams	28.35
grams	pounds	0.0022	pounds	grams	453.6
kilograms	pounds	2.205	pounds	kilograms	0.4536
kilograms	stone	0.158	stone	kilograms	6.35
kilograms	hundredweight	0.01968	hundredweight	kilograms	50.8
kilograms	tons	0.00098	tons	kilograms	1016
tonnes	tons	0.9842	tons	tonnes	1.016
square cm	square inches	0.155	sq. inches	square cm	6.45
square m	square yards	1.196	square yards	square m	0.8361
square m	acres	0.00025	acres	square m	4047
hectares	acres	2.471	acres	hectares	0.4047
square km	square miles	0.386	square miles	square km	2.59
cubic cm (ml)	fluid ounces	0.0352	fluid ounces	cubic cm (ml)	28.41
litres	pints	1.76	pints	litres	0.568
litres	gallons	0.22	gallons	litres	4.546
km per hour	miles per hour	0.625	miles per hour	km per hour	1.6
m per second	miles per hour	2.2374	miles per hour	m per second	0.4469

S

To convert degrees Fahrenheit to degrees Celsius: $C = \frac{5}{9}(F - 32)$

To convert degrees Celsius to degrees Fahrenheit: $F = \frac{9}{5}C + 32$

MATHSFACT

The metric system began in the closing years of the 18th century in France as the need for standard measures became important. The words *metre* and *metric* come from the Greek word *metron* meaning *a measure*.

11+

TYPES OF ANGLE

Angles can be any size from 0° to 360°. They are given special names according to their size.

size of angle (degrees)	name
less than 90	acute
90	right
90 to 180	obtuse
180	straight
180 to 360	reflex

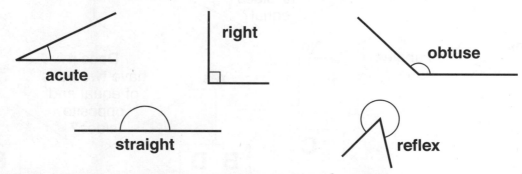

R

Some former pupils of mine once suggested a mnemonic for remembering the order of these names: Always Run Over Stupid Robins! Well, you don't forget it.

Knowing the approximate size of each type of angle helps with estimation, especially in bearings questions. It is good practice to sketch a scale diagram out in rough before you draw it accurately with the exact angles, to make sure that you don't run out of paper!

COMPASS POINTS

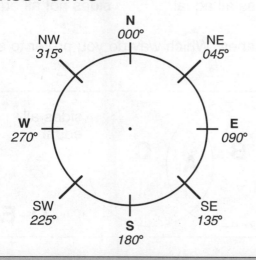

Bearings are always given clockwise from north, and are always given as a three-digit number.

Try to get used to estimating angles before drawing or measuring them, in order to prevent the mistake of reading the wrong scale on your angle measurer or protractor.

S

MATHSFACT

It is not clear why it was chosen to divide the circle up into 360 degrees, although it was done by the Greeks and Babylonians. The most likely suggestion is that it was because 360 has so many different factors.

11+

On this page we use a flow chart to sort six different quadrilaterals (can you name them all?) and then we sort them, in a different way, using a Carroll Diagram.

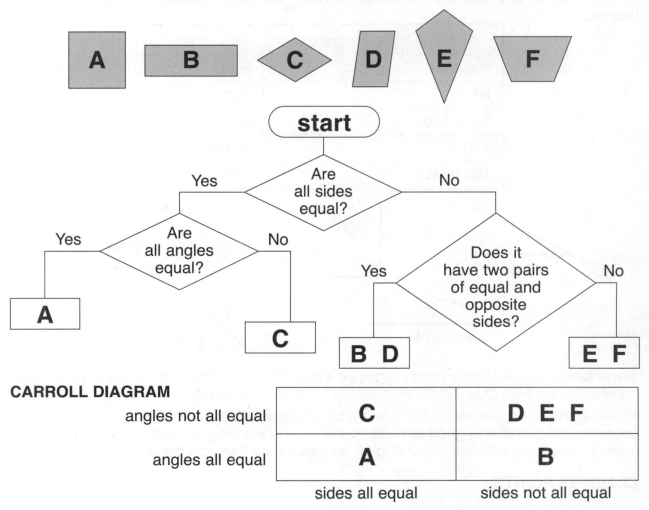

R

CARROLL DIAGRAM

	sides all equal	sides not all equal
angles not all equal	C	D E F
angles all equal	A	B

Finally we use a Venn Diagram to sort the shapes. Which way do you prefer to sort the quadrilaterals?

VENN DIAGRAM

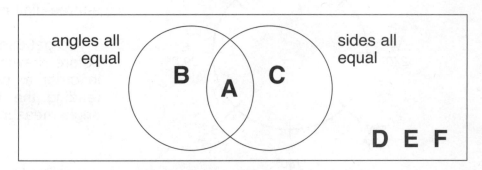

D

MATHSFACT

Lewis Carroll wrote a song entitled *The Lobster Quadrille* in chapter 10 of his book *Alice in Wonderland*. A quadrille was a very complicated square dance in five sequences or figures.

TRIANGULAR NUMBERS

At the start of a game of snooker there are fifteen reds in the triangle.

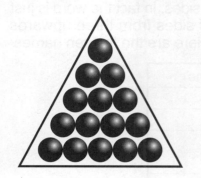

Which other numbers of balls could be arranged in a triangle in this way?

The answer is a sequence of numbers which we call the triangular numbers.

They come up a lot in mathematics.

13+

Here are the first ten triangular numbers:

n	T_n
1	1
2	3
3	6
4	10
5	15
6	21
7	28
8	36
9	45
10	55

In the table, T_n simply means the *nth triangular number*.

Notice how they go up:

+2, +3, +4, +5 etc. added on to the one before.

Also notice that any two consecutive **triangular** numbers give a sum which is a **square** number, e.g. 21 + 28 = 49

In general though, we can jump to any triangular number we want simply by using this formula:

$$T_n = \tfrac{1}{2}n(n+1)$$

R

The sum of two consecutive triangular numbers is a square number.

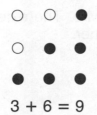

3 + 6 = 9

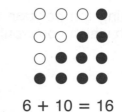

6 + 10 = 16

N/A

MATHSFACT

Many other types of numbers have been given shape names. Examples include such rarely used ones as *Pentagonal Numbers*, *Hexagonal Numbers*, and even *Pyramidal Numbers*!

89

POLYGON NAMES AND ANGLE PROPERTIES

NAMES OF THE POLYGONS

A polygon is nothing more complicated than a shape with straight sides. In fact the word is just the Greek for *many sides*. Polygons can have any number of sides from three upwards and each number of sides has a corresponding special name. Here are the first ten names:

number of sides	polygon name
3	triangle
4	quadrilateral
5	pentagon
6	hexagon
7	heptagon
8	octagon
9	nonagon
10	decagon
11	hendecagon
12	dodecagon

REGULAR POLYGON ANGLES

A regular polygon is one in which all the sides are the same length and all the angles are equal. These are made by drawing the required number of points at equal intervals round the circumference of a circle.

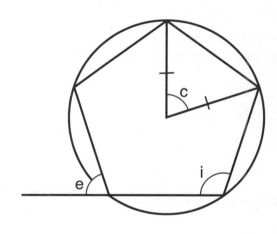

This is a regular pentagon, but the following rules work for any regular polygon.

Let's assume that the polygon has n sides. (Here $n = 5$)

Then the angle at the centre is given by $c = \frac{360°}{n}$.

The triangle made by joining the centre of the circle to any two vertices is always isosceles. From this fact it is easy to show that the interior angle formula is:

$$i = 180° - c$$
$$= 180° - \frac{360°}{n}$$

Imagine making the polygon out of a straight length of wire. The exterior angle is the angle through which you would bend the wire at each corner.

$$e = 180° - i$$
$$= \frac{360°}{n} = c$$

Finally for any polygon, the sum of all the interior angles is given by $180(n - 2)°$.

> **MATHSFACT**
>
> The more sides a polygon has, the closer it gets to being a circle. In fact, if you accurately drew a regular polygon with just 36 sides, most people would think it was a circle given just a quick glance.

AREA AND VOLUME FORMULAE

You are not given a sheet of formulae for Common Entrance, so if you want to do the calculations then you have to learn them for yourself. It's not hard to do, and you probably know most of them already.

AREA FORMULAE

13+

square
$A = a^2$

rectangle
$A = lw$

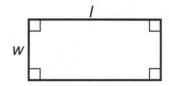

triangle
$A = \frac{1}{2}bh$

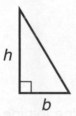

parallelogram
$A = bh$

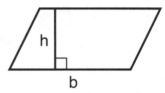

trapezium
$A = \frac{1}{2}(a + b)h$

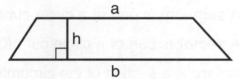

circle
$A = \pi r^2$

VOLUME FORMULAE

cube: $V = a^3$ cuboid: $V = lwh$
(edge-length cubed)   (length × width × height)

prism: volume = cross section area × height (length). This includes cylinders!

pyramid: $\frac{1}{3}$ × base area × height. This includes cones!

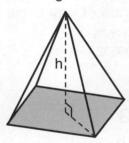

pyramid volume = $\frac{1}{3}$ × base area × height

MATHSFACT

News is coming in of a new Pi Memorisation Record. Hiroyuki Goto had held the record for many years with 42 195 places, but fellow countryman Akira Haraguchi recently recited 100 000 places. This was his fourth attempt. Previously he got lost after 50 000 digits and had to start again; before that his attempt was ended early by the caretaker who wanted to lock up for the night.

The **circumference** of the circle is the same as its perimeter – it is the distance all the way around the edge.

The **diameter** is any straight line which goes from one side of the circle to the other, through the centre. The diameter divides the circle into two equal halves.

The **radius** is any straight line which runs from the centre of the circle to the circumference.

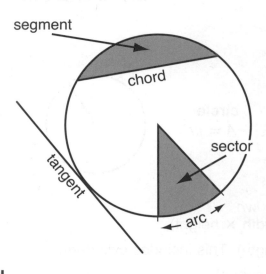

A **chord** is a straight line joining any two points on the circumference.

A **segment** is part of a circle cut off by a chord.

A **sector** is part of a circle cut off by two radii.

An **arc** is a section of the circumference.

A **tangent** is a straight line which just touches the circumference.

A **semicircle** is half a circle, cut at the diameter.

PI

The famous number which is calculated by dividing the circumference of any circle by its diameter. Its approximate value is 3.14 or $\frac{22}{7}$ or $\frac{355}{113}$ or even $\frac{312689}{99532}$!

Let's give it a few more decimal places. How about the first fifty?

$$\pi = 3.14159265358979323846264338327950288419716939937511 \text{ to 50 d.p.}$$

MATHSFACT

The value of Pi (3.14159......) has been calculated to over one **trillion** decimal places. Professor Kanada of Tokyo University and his team have claimed a new record of 1 241 100 000 000 places (Dec 2002) after 600 hours' number crunching on a Japanese super-computer. It still doesn't repeat.

SET NOTATION AND VENN DIAGRAMS

A list of signs and symbols used in describing sets:

 $\in$ is a member (element) of

 $\notin$ is not a member of

 $\cup$ union: elements in either one set or the other (or both) are included

 $\cap$ intersection: only elements in **both** sets are included

 $\subset$ is a subset of

 $\supset$ contains

 $\varnothing$ the empty set (contains no elements)

 A' complement: those items **not** in set A

 $\mathscr{E}$ the universal set: this set contains all elements under consideration

We list the elements in a set within curly brackets, e.g. $A = \{a, e, i, o, u\}$.

We count the number of elements in a set using $n\,(\ )$, as in $n\,(A) = 5$ for the set A above.

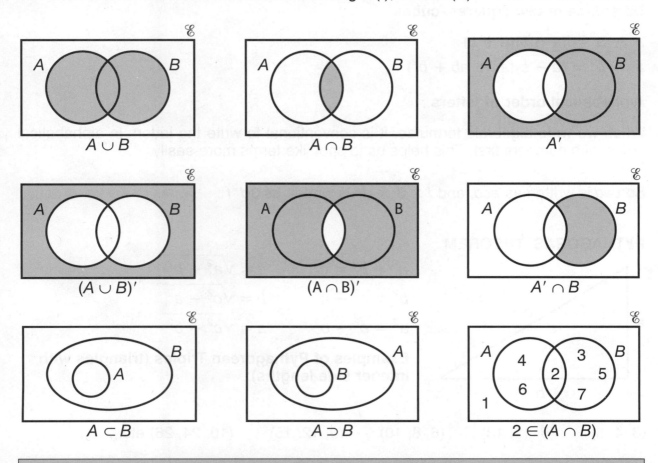

MATHSFACT

A Venn Diagram has a region for every possible combination of the sets being studied. With two or three sets, these are easily displayed using overlapping circles but, with four or more, they become very hard to draw!

COMMON ALGEBRAIC FORMULAE

Multiplying out brackets

$a(x + y) = ax + ay$

$a(x - y) = ax - ay$

$(a + b)(x + y) = ax + ay + bx + by$

$(a + b)(x - y) = ax - ay + bx - by$

$(a - b)(x + y) = ax + ay - bx - by$

$(a - b)(x - y) = ax - ay - bx + by$

NOTE THE SIGNS!

Squaring a bracket

$(a + b)^2 = a^2 + 2ab + b^2$

$(a - b)^2 = a^2 - 2ab + b^2$

$(a + b + c)^2 = a^2 + ab + ac + ab + b^2 + bc + ac + bc + c^2$

$$= a^2 + b^2 + c^2 + 2ab + 2ac + 2bc$$

Difference of two squares/cubes

$a^2 - b^2 = (a - b)(a + b)$

$a^3 - b^3 = (a - b)(a^2 + ab + b^2)$

Alphabetical order of letters

When we write algebraic formulae, it is conventional to write the letters in alphabetical order, with numbers first. This helps us to spot like terms more easily.

So *cad* is written as *acd*, and $f \times 3 \times d^2$ is written as $3d^2f$

PYTHAGORAS' THEOREM

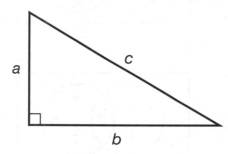

$a^2 + b^2 = c^2$ $\qquad c = \sqrt{a^2 + b^2}$

$b^2 = c^2 - a^2$ $\qquad b = \sqrt{c^2 - a^2}$

$a^2 = c^2 - b^2$ $\qquad a = \sqrt{c^2 - b^2}$

Examples of Pythagorean Triples (triangles with integer side lengths):

(3, 4, 5)   (5, 12, 13)   (6, 8, 10)   (9, 12, 15)   (10, 24, 26) etc.

MATHSFACT

James Garfield was the only US President to make a contribution to mathematics. He discovered a new proof of Pythagoras' Theorem.

REVISION GUIDELINES

1. Revise regularly over a long period of time, rather than at the last minute. Six months before the examination is not too early to start!

2. Revise actively, not passively: practise recently-learned techniques either with past papers or made-up questions; use underlines, highlights and margin notes in this book; write your own summaries in the NOTES section or on index cards. You could even create your own webpage or on-screen presentation!

3. Do not try to revise for too long at a stretch; two or three topics revised in half an hour is time well spent; two hours spent with your head in this book would be hard going, uninteresting and probably unproductive. You have to keep your mind fresh and interested.

4. Revise with a friend – it's fun! Test each other as you go and you will really find yourselves learning quickly. Surprisingly, the best revision is achieved by **recalling** rather than **relearning**.

5. Be disciplined with your revision. Try revising at the same time each day / week. Allow yourself no distractions (e.g. television) while revising, but if you honestly work better with a little music in the background then fair enough. Some people find that a useful strategy is varying the **location** where they revise.

R

6. Set yourself little 'goals' as you work, e.g. a biscuit when you have finished this or a play outside when you have finished that. This helps to break up the revision into more manageable chunks and improves your focus and concentration.

7. Remind yourself regularly how much you know in order to keep up both your confidence and your motivation. *Nobody* knows nothing; as you revise you will see your knowledge increase dramatically.

MATHSFACT
The UK Pi Memorisation Record currently stands at 22 000 places by David Hammet (March 2004). For school-age children, the current records are 628 places by Colm MacQueen Year 10 (Scotland, Jan 2003), 610 places by Leo Davidson Year 6 (England, Jul 2001) and 203 places by Daniel Hough Year 10 (Wales, Jun 2001).

EXAMINATION GUIDELINES

1. Make sure you sleep well the night before the examination. Last-minute cramming is not as useful as a good rest.

2. When you see the paper, read it through quickly to get an overall feel for its length. Start with one of your favourite topics to get you in a more relaxed mood.

3. When you tackle a question, do not spend too long on it, but make sure you read it carefully to ensure you understand exactly what is wanted. It is very easy to miss the word 'not' in a probability question, or the words 'as a percentage' in a number question.

4. Show all your working! In a non-calculator question, failure to do this could result in loss of marks; in a calculator question it helps the examiner to check your method even if the final answer is wrong. Candidates often forget that marks can be awarded for working – it's not just about getting the right answer.

5. Is your answer reasonable? A building 7 cm tall, or an average pupil mass of 987 kg, should make you think again. The most common way to get a crazy answer is to forget the **units** (centimetres and metres in the same question for example).

6. If you have time at the end, use it to check through your answers. We all make sillly mistakes!

7. Once you have handed in your paper, forget about it! You have done your best, and you can't improve it by worrying. Just look forward to results day, when you will see how well you revised, and when you will hear the congratulatory cheers of all your friends!

MATHSFACT
A $1 000 000 reward awaits the person who can solve the famous maths problem called the Riemann Hypothesis. All you have to do is to find a pattern in the way that prime numbers are arranged. Be warned, though – people have been looking for hundreds of years already!

GLOSSARY (DICTIONARY) AND INDEX

Key:

o	11+ words and general knowledge
oo	13+ words (core syllabus)
ooo	13+ words (extended syllabus)

Please note that these age codes are offered as guidelines only!

Page references in **bold** are principal references. Look these up first.
Page references in *italics* are references to MathsFacts.

I suggest that you colour in the little circles when you know the word!

age code	word and meaning	page reference
o	**abacus** the predecessor of the electronic calculator: a device usually consisting of rows of beads on wires to assist with mental calculations	
o	**acre** a measurement of area in the imperial (old) system of units (about 4000 m^2)	**86**
o	**acute angle** an angle less than 90 degrees	**87**
o	**add** plus; find the total	**3**
o	**addition** the process of adding; a 'sum'	**3**, 10, *37*, 41, 45
o	**adjacent** next to; side by side; in a right-angled triangle the side which is not 'opposite' (to a given angle) adjacent	79, **85**
oo	**algebra** the branch of mathematics using letters to stand for numbers	**41**, **42**, *42*, 48, 49, 71, *71*, 72, *72*, 73, 74, 75, 94
oo	**algebraic expression** one or more algebraic terms combined using + and − e.g. 5 + 2 − x	42
oo	**alternate angles** angles in an angle diagram which are in a 'Z' or 'N' shape	53
o	**am (a.m.)** (Latin) *ante meridiem* means 'before noon'; *see also* **pm (p.m.)**	83
o	**amount** quantity; how much or how many	

MATHSFACT

Shuffle two separate packs of cards. Now play a game of *snap* with a friend by turning up the top card of your pile at the same time as he does with his pile. Announce that he loses only if you get an **identical** match as you deal the pairs of cards out. Unlikely? You will win more times than he does!

G/I

age code	word and meaning	page reference
O	**angle** the amount in degrees by which two joined lines have been 'hinged open'	12, 19, **53**, 57, 62, 85, **87**, 90
O	**angle measurer** an instrument such as a protractor for measuring the sizes of angles	**87**
OO	**angles at a point** two or more angles sharing a common vertex with an angle sum of 360° $a + b + c = 360°$	**53**
OO	**angles in a triangle** the three angles in the same triangle always add up to 180°; in a right-angled triangle this is equivalent to saying that the other two angles always add up to 90° $a + b + c = 180°$ $d + e = 90°$	**53**
OO	**angles on a straight line** two or more angles sharing a common edge with an angle sum of 180° $f + g = 180°$	**53**
O	**answer** that which was sought by the question	
O	**anticlockwise** an opposite direction to that in which the hands of a clock turn	*55*
OOO	**apex** the highest point in a plane or solid shape	**12**
OO	**approximately** by way of an approximation; roughly	
OO	**approximately equal to (≈)** roughly the same as; having used approximate rather than exact values	39
OO	**approximation** a 'rough' answer, often used as a check to a calculator result	39
OOO	**arc** a section of the circumference of a circle	**12**
O	**area** the amount of space inside a flat shape, commonly measured in square centimetres (cm^2), square metres (m^2), hectares (ha) etc.	**18**, *73*

G/I

MATHSFACT

When asked to think of a number between 1 and 10, most people think of the number 7.

When asked to think of a number between 1 and 4, most people think of the number 3.

age code	word and meaning	page reference
OO	**area factor** the old area was multiplied by this to obtain the new area; the area factor is the square of the scale factor scale factor 2 → area factor 4	**60**, *60*
O	**arithmetic** the branch of mathematics dealing with numbers, especially with +, −, ×, ÷	**1**, **3**, 10, 27, 28, 30, 37, 40, 41, 45, *53*
OO	**arithmetic sequence** a sequence of numbers which goes up (or down) by the same amount each time, e.g. 1, 4, 7, 10, …	**47**, 72
O	**arrangement** a way of putting things in an order or an 'array' – a pattern	6, **68**
OO	**arrowhead** the only concave quadrilateral; delta or nested V-shape	**57**
O	**ascending** going up; increasing in order of size	
O	**average** a calculation used to summarise a set of data	22, **23**
OOO	**average speed** the total distance travelled divided by the total time taken	**78**
O	**axes** plural form of **axis**	**9**
O	**axis** a line on a grid holding the numbers or scale, usually horizontal (*x*-axis) and vertical (*y*-axis)	**9**
OOO	**axis of rotation symmetry** imagine a CD spinning around a pencil – the pencil is the axis of rotation	
OO	**axis of symmetry** also known as the **line of symmetry**	13, **54**
O	**balance (1)** the remainder after a series of financial payments (in and out)	
O	**balance (2)** an old-fashioned pair of weighing scales: if the scales balanced then the masses were equal	
O	**bank balance** the amount of money in the bank	**10**

MATHSFACT

The famous Rubik's Cube puzzle has 432 520 032 274 489 856 000 different positions.

age code	word and meaning	page reference
O	**bar chart** a diagram which shows data by the height or length of the bar	63, **64**
O	**bar-line graph** as a bar chart, but using lines or sticks, usually to represent frequency (also called a 'stick graph')	64
O	**base** the bottom face of a solid shape or the lower edge of a plane shape	
OO	**base angles** especially in an isosceles triangle – the two angles which are equal *(NB base angles are not necessarily at the bottom of the picture!)*	
O	**bearings** a 3-figure direction measured clockwise in degrees from north N N N 040° 120° 270°	19, **62**, 87
O	**best estimate** the answer which is closest to the exact answer without having to work it out	
O	**between** somewhere along the line from one to the other	
OO	**bias** a tendency to go one way more than another; favouritism	
OO	**biased** a die, spinner or coin is biased if it is not fair	
O	**BIDMAS** (*see* **BODMAS**)	
OO	**billion** one thousand million, written as 1 000 000 000	*24, 35*
OO	**bisect** cut into two equal halves: the two diagonals of a rectangle, square, rhombus and parallelogram bisect each other	**57**
OO	**bisector** a line which cuts something in half, commonly an angle or another line	
O	**BODMAS** **B**rackets, **O**f, **D**ivision, **M**ultiplication, **A**ddition, **S**ubtraction – a way to remember the priorities of arithmetical operations. *(Some people prefer **BIDMAS**, where the second letter is for **I**ndices.)*	**41**, *41*, 48

G/I

MATHSFACT

One way to measure the complexity of a board game is to work out the number of possible positions. Draughts has about 10^{12} positions, while chess has 10^{42} positions. The ancient game of Go, however, has 10^{170} positions!

age code	word and meaning	page reference
O	**brackets** another name for parentheses '(' and ')'; see also **factorise** and **multiply out**	**94**
O	**calculate** work out; evaluate *(It does not always mean use a calculator!)*	
O	**calculation** the process of finding the value of a numerical expression	
O	**calculator** any machine which makes calculations easier	1, 50, **52**
OO	**cancel** cross out, usually in pairs, and especially when simplifying fractions or ratios $\quad$ e.g. $\frac{\overset{2}{4}}{\underset{3}{6}} \rightarrow \frac{2}{3} \qquad \overset{3}{6} : \overset{1}{2} \quad 3 : 1$	**28**, 45
OO	**cancellation** the process of simplifying which involves dividing by a common factor $\quad \overset{1}{6}x = \overset{2}{12} \\ \rightarrow x = 2$	
O	**capacity** the amount of space taken up or enclosed by a solid; the volume	
O	**Carroll diagram** a two-way table used to help with classification, e.g. Girls (G) / Boys (B) against Swimmers (S) / Non-Swimmers (N) (named after Lewis Carroll)	88
O	**Celsius** the temperature scale, also known as centigrade, on which water freezes at 0 degrees and boils at 100 degrees	8, **10**, 86
O	**centilitre** one hundredth of a litre	**17**
O	**centimetre** one hundredth part of a metre	**17**, 18, 86
O	**centre** the middle	
OO	**centre of enlargement** the point from which the enlargement is constructed; the 'focus' or 'vanishing point'	**59**
OO	**centre of rotation** the part of the picture which does not move when the picture is rotated, e.g. the hub of a wheel	**55**
O	**century** a period of time lasting one hundred years	
O	**certain** having a probability of 1; impossible to fail; guaranteed to happen	**26**

G/I

age code	word and meaning	page reference
O	**chance**　another word for probability or likelihood	*23*, **26**
O	**change (money)**　the amount of money required to make up the cost of the purchases to the value of the cash offered	
O	**chart**　a picture which helps to represent a set of data	**63**
OOO	**chord**　a straight line joining any two points on the circumference of a circle	**92**
O	**circle**　the round shape made by joining up all points a fixed distance from the centre	58, 61, 87, **90**, *90*, **91, 92**
OO	**circumference**　the perimeter of a circle	**58**, **92**
OO	**class interval**　the size of the group (when data is grouped), e.g. 20 to 25 cm has a class interval (width) of 5 cm	24
O	**classify**　sort out according to the properties of the items; books can be classified by genre, shapes can be classified by number of sides etc.	88
O	**clear (display, entry)**　reset a calculator to receive the number again (C) or the whole calculation again (AC)	
O	**clock (1)**　12-hour clocks tell the time using only hours 1 to 12 but also with am or pm	**83**
O	**clock (2)**　24-hour clocks tell the time using hours 00.00 to 23.59; times after 12.00 are pm times	**83**
O	**clockwise**　the same direction as that turned by the hands of a clock	*55, 62*, **83**
OO	**coefficient**　the number in front of a letter or term, especially in an equation, e.g. $3x^2$ or $24x$	**74**
OO	**collect like terms**　group together terms in algebra with the same letter part, e.g. $3ab + 4a + 2ab = 4a + 5ab$	**42**
O	**column**　the vertical in a table (up – down)	
OO	**common factor**　a factor which is shared by two or more numbers or terms, e.g. 5 is a common factor of 15 and 95, and 4 is a common factor of $4a$ and $8b$	**42**

G/I

MATHSFACT

Take any three digit number (say 126), reverse it (621) and subtract the smaller from the larger (621 − 126 = 495). Reverse the answer (594) and add the two (495 + 594 = 1089). What did you get?

age code	word and meaning	page reference
O	**compare** put one thing against another to see how similar or different they are	**23**
O	**compass** a direction finder marked as N, NE, E, SE, S, SW, W, NW	**19**, 62, 87
O	**compasses** geometrical instrument for drawing circles; also used to draw arcs when constructing triangles	**12**, 58
OO	**complementary angles** two angles which add up to 90 degrees $a + b = 90°$	**53**
OO	**complements** fits the gap left by the other, especially in the context of complementary angles	
OO	**composite (1)** a shape made up from other simpler shapes	**61**, 77
OO	**composite (2)** a number which is not prime	4, **31**
OO	**concave** curving in (think 'caving in') like a letter C; the opposite to **convex**	
OOO	**conclude** sum up the main points of a reasoned argument or proof	
OO	**conclusion** the summary statement made from consideration of the statistics (figures and graphs) in the question	21, 22, **23**, 24, 25, 63, 65, 69, 71
OOO	**cone** a circular-based pyramid	**77**
O	**congruence** the property of being congruent	11, **13**
O	**congruent** identical in size and shape	11, **13**
OO	**conjugate** two angles which add up to 360 degrees; compare with **complementary** and **supplementary** $a + b = 360°$	

G/I

MATHSFACT

Arranging numbers in ALPHABETICAL rather than numerical order can be very interesting: EIGHT likes to come first all the time, and TWO is content to bring up the rear. FIVE is sometimes the only one in its correct place.

age code	word and meaning	page reference
O	**consecutive** following on in counting order, e.g. 4, 5, 6 are consecutive numbers	**89**
OO	**construct** draw accurately a geometrical figure using ruler and compasses	**12**, 59, 62
OO	**construction lines** lines left on a construction to show where the compasses and ruler were used	**12**, 59
O	**continue** carry on in the same way as before	
OO	**continuous** without jumps or gaps; a measurement which allows 'in between' values	
O	**conversion graph** a straight line graph used to convert between one unit and another, for example metric and imperial	**25**, 86
O	**convert** change from one into another, especially from one unit of measurement to another	**25**
OO	**convex** bulging outwards like a letter D; the opposite to **concave**	
O	**co-ordinate pair** two numbers (*x*, *y*) used to plot a point on a co-ordinate grid	**9**
O	**co-ordinate point** the point plotted by a co-ordinate pair such as (2, 4)	**9**
O	**co-ordinates** pairs of numbers used to indicate positions on a grid; (*x*, *y*) = (across, up)	**9**, 43, *43*, 69
OO	**correlation** describes the way one measurement increases relative to another; see also **positive (2)** and **negative (2)**	**69**
O	**corresponding (points)** if a shape has been transformed (e.g. by translation) then each vertex has a Start and Finish position; these two positions make a pair of corresponding points / vertices	**11**, 59
OO	**corresponding (angles)** in an angle diagram, the equal angles formed by a straight line crossing a pair of parallel lines ('F-ANGLES')	**53**

G/I

MATHSFACT

One of the world's oldest unsolved problems in mathematics, known as Fermat's Last Theorem (Fermat died in 1665), was finally cracked in 1996 by British mathematician Andrew Wiles in a 150-page proof.

age code	word and meaning	page reference
OOO	**cosine (cos)** in a right-angled triangle, the cosine of an angle is equal to the ratio adjacent : hypotenuse or adjacent ÷ hypotenuse	79
OOO	**counter-example** an example which breaks the rule; the rule 'all prime numbers are odd' has a counter-example in the number 2 which is prime but even	
OO	**cross-section** the flat shape you get when you slice open a solid	
O	**cube (solid shape)** a solid with six square faces	*8*, 11, **18**, 91
O	**cube (number)** the result of multiplying a number by its square	*60*, **82**
OO	**cube root** (e.g. $\sqrt[3]{8}$) the number which, when cubed, gives the number you started with, e.g. the cube root of 8 is 2	**82**
O	**cubed** a number which has been multiplied by its square, e.g. 2 cubed is 8 and 3 cubed is 27	**82**
O	**cubic centimetre** the volume of a cube which is one centimetre along each straight edge; a unit of volume, equivalent to one ml of liquid	**18**, 86
O	**cubic metre** the volume of a cube which is one metre along each straight edge; one cubic metre of water has a mass of one tonne	**18**
O	**cubic millimetre** the volume of a cube which is one millimetre along each straight edge; about the size of a grain of sugar	**18**
O	**cuboid** a solid shape which is a rectangular version of a cube	**11**, 18, 56, 91
O	**currency** the type of money (e.g. pounds, euros, dollars) used by a country	**25**
O	**curve** a line between two points, not necessarily the shortest route; a line drawn through several points on a graph	**25**

G/I

MATHSFACT

It is interesting that there are 52 cards in a pack. If you spell out letter by letter the names of the cards in a suit from A-C-E to K-I-N-G then the last card is dealt out as you spell the last letter!

age code	word and meaning	page reference
ooo	**cylinder** a solid shape which is a circular prism	58, **77**, 91
o	**data** information, results etc. (often collected by a survey)	**21, 22**, 23, **24, 25**, 63, 64, 65
o	**data collection sheet** a table designed to collect the results of a questionnaire, observation or survey in an efficient manner	
o	**database** an information system, usually electronic, used to store and display details of a collection of things such as books, volcanoes or football players	
o	**day** a period of time lasting twenty-four hours	
o	**decade** a period of time lasting ten years	
oo	**decagon** a polygon with ten sides	**90**
oo	**decimal fraction (decimal)** a fraction expressed as a decimal, e.g. one quarter is 0.25 as a decimal fraction	**44**
o	**decimal number** a number with any number of figures after the decimal point e.g. 13.502	3, *28*
o	**decimal places** the number of digits after the decimal point, e.g. 3.1415 has four decimal places	3, **28**, 35, 50
o	**decimal point** the dot between the units column and the tenths column T U · t 1 0 · 5	1, **3**, *3*, 28
oo	**decision tree diagram** a type of flow chart used for sorting or making decisions yes blue? no	88
o	**decrease** make smaller	
oo	**deduce** use logic to make a conclusion or deduction	
oo	**definition** a precise explanation of a word or phrase	
o	**degree (°) (angles)** the unit of measurement for the size of an angle, e.g. 90 degrees make a right angle, 360 degrees make a full turn	12, 53, 62, 65, 85, **87**, *87*, 90

G/I

MATHSFACT

The humble egg is a masterpiece of mathematical engineering. Its shape is the strongest structure possible using eggshell – so strong that you would find it impossible to crush a fresh hen's egg by squeezing the ends together in your hands.

age code	word and meaning	page reference
O	**degree (°) (temperature)** the unit of measurement for temperature	8, **10**, 86
OOO	**degree of accuracy** a way of describing the reliability of a measurement, e.g. 'to the nearest centimetre'	
O	**degree Celsius** the unit of temperature using a scale on which lie 0 °C (water freezing) and 100 °C (water boiling)	**8**, 10, 86
O	**degree Fahrenheit** the unit of temperature using a scale on which lie 32 °F (water freezing) and 212 °F (water boiling)	**8**, 86
OO	**delta** another name for an arrowhead or concave kite	**57**
O	**denominator** the bottom number in a proper, improper or algebraic fraction $\frac{3}{4}$ $\frac{8}{5}$ $\frac{ab}{3c}$	**33**, 40, 44
OOO	**density** a way of comparing the masses of the same volume of two substances; density = mass ÷ volume, e.g. water has a density of 1 g/cm^3, iron has a density of approx. 7 g/cm^3, lead has a density of approx. 12 g/cm^3	
O	**deposit** a payment made at the beginning of a deal, which can either be returned later or count as a first payment	
O	**depth** how deep something is; usually a vertical measurement of distance starting at zero and increasing downwards	
O	**descending** going down; numbers in decreasing order	
O	**diagonal** a line across a plane shape joining two vertices (corners)	**57**
O	**diagram** a picture used to illustrate a situation, especially to make a complex problem clearer	**63**
OO	**diameter** a chord through the centre of a circle, cutting the circle in half	*50*, 58, *61*, **92**

G/I

MATHSFACT

Henry Dudeney (1847–1930, English) and Sam Loyd (1841–1911, American) both delighted their readers with a huge variety of original mathematical puzzles, many of which involved areas to be 'dissected' – cut up and formed into different and surprising shapes.

age code	word and meaning	page reference
o	**dice, die** one die, two dice: the (usually) cube-shaped solid used in games and probability experiments	66, **68**
o	**difference** the answer to a subtraction	**6**, *36*, 46, 72, 73
ooo	**difference of two squares / cubes** a useful result in algebra which makes factorisation easier, e.g. $x^2 - y^2 \rightarrow (x + y)(x - y)$	**94**
oo	**difference pattern** the way in which the differences between terms of a sequence change as the sequence continues; this process, known as the 'difference method' will show up almost every hidden pattern in a sequence	**46**
o	**digit (1)** one of the symbols from 0 to 9 used in writing numbers	**1**, *9, 11, 21, 82*
o	**digit (2)** another word for a finger especially when used to help counting.	
oo	**dimension** a measurement of length, width or height	**11**, *18*, 56, *56, 77*
o	**direction** the way to be regarded as 'forwards', especially using the points of a compass or a 3-figure bearing	19
o	**discount** a reduction in the usual price	
o	**discrete** a measurement which can only take certain values, going up in 'jumps'	**21**, 22, 23, 64
o	**display (calculator)** the area on a calculator used to show the numbers entered and the calculation result	51
o	**distance** the length of a line between two points	**78**, *78*
oo	**distance-time graph** a graph used to illustrate a journey	
o	**distribution** the way in which a set of data falls into groups in a frequency table	23, 63
o	**divide** share; the **first** number is the one being shared	1, 27, **28**, 30, **33**, 34, **39**, **40**, 41, 45
ooo	**dividend (1)** a big number which is being divided up by a smaller number (divisor)	*36*

MATHSFACT

Scientifically speaking, a second is actually defined as the time interval of 9192631770 resonance vibration cycles of a Caesium-133 atom. In approximately one second, a pulse of light (or a radio wave) can travel to the Moon.

age code	word and meaning	page reference
ooo	**dividend (2)** a reward paid out to shareholders (investors) by a company when it wants to share out the profits	
oo	**divisibility** the property of being divisible by a number other than one	
o	**divisible** can be divided by, e.g. 12 is divisible by 4	**7**
o	**division (1)** the operation of sharing one number equally into smaller parts	39, **40**, *41*
o	**division (2)** the interval on a measuring scale	**15**
oo	**divisor** when 24 is divided by 3 to get 8, 3 is called the divisor (24 is the *dividend* and 8 is the *quotient*; there is no *remainder*)	*36*
oo	**dodecagon** a polygon with twelve sides; a regular dodecagon has twelve equal sides and twelve equal angles	**90**
oo	**dodecahedron** a solid with twelve faces	**23**, *30*
o	**double (verb)** multiply by two	*32*
o	**double (noun)** the result of multiplying by two, as in '6 is the double of 3'	*32*
o	**doubt** includes the possibility of failure as well as success	
o	**draw (1)** to draw in mathematics requires pencil, compasses and ruler	
o	**draw (2)** an even score at the end of a game	
o	**draw (3)** select a card (at random) from a pack	
o	**east** towards the direction of the rising sun, usually shown as towards the right on a map	**19**, 87
o	**edge (1)** the line joining two adjacent vertices in a polygon (also called a side); 'all the way around the edge' refers to the perimeter of the shape 3 edges	**18**
o	**edge (2)** the line shared by two adjacent faces in a 3-D shape, running from one vertex to another 12 edges	**11**, *30*
o	**eighths** the result when a whole is divided into eight equal pieces	**5**

G/I

MATHSFACT

The well-known children's author, Lewis Carroll, who wrote *Alice in Wonderland* and *Through the Looking Glass*, was in fact the Revd. Charles L. Dodgson, a mathematics lecturer at Oxford University in the 1800s.

age code	word and meaning	page reference
OO	**elements of a set** members of a group which share the same property, e.g. in the set {vowels} are the elements {a, e, i, o, u}	70, **93**
OO	**elevation** the view of a three-dimensional solid from either the front/back or sides	
OO	**enlarge** make bigger	**59**, 60
OO	**enlargement** a transformation which changes the size of a shape to make a similar image	**59**, 60
O	**enter (calculator)** type in a calculation or command by a sequence of keystrokes; the final button then pressed	
OO	**equal angles** one of many situations in geometry in which two or more angles in a diagram are the same e.g.	**53**, **85**, 90
OO	**equal sides** sides which are the same length, as in isosceles or equilateral triangles, many quadrilaterals and all regular shapes	**85**, 90
O	**equally likely** having the same chance or probability	
O	**equals (=)** the expressions on either side have the same value	**48**, *48*
OO	**equation** an expression with '=' in it, usually to be solved	43, **48**, 49, *49*, 71, *71*, 74, *74*
OO	**equidistant** the same distance away	
O	**equilateral** all sides of equal length, e.g. equilateral triangle	*30*, 53, **85**
OOO	**equivalence** even better than being equal, e.g. $8x = 40$ is only true when $x = 5$; equivalence, however, is always true; e.g. $8x \equiv 5x + 3x$	

G/I

MATHSFACT

'Like the crest of a peacock so is mathematics at the head of all knowledge' (old Indian saying)

age code	word and meaning	page reference
o	**equivalent** two things which are the same in every way, especially fractions and ratios, e.g. $\frac{2}{4} \equiv \frac{4}{8}$ $4 : 12 \equiv 1 : 3$	**5**, 34, 40, 42, 44
o	**estimate** make a reasonable guess at the answer without detailed calculation	**39**, 51
oo	**evaluate** work out exactly, using a reliable method of calculation	
o	**even** a number which ends in 0, 2, 4, 6 or 8	2, 7, **84**
o	**even chance** the probability of 50%, as in 'heads or tails'	23, **26**, 66
oo	**event** one of any number of possible outcomes or future happenings	**66**
oo	**evidence** supporting material for a generalisation, but evidence alone does not make a proof	
oo	**exact** no further accuracy is possible	
oo	**exactly** the true answer, with no inaccuracies or approximations	
oo	**exchange rate** the figures used to convert one currency into another	
ooo	**exhaustive** every possibility has been listed	
oo	**experiment** any trial which has at least one outcome	**66**
oo	**experimental probability** the experimental probability of getting a head on a coin is (number of heads counted ÷ (number of times coin was tossed); this gets closer to the Theoretical Probability the more trials are done	**66**
o	**explain** give a reason for something, especially using the word 'because' in the answer	
o	**explore** investigate an unknown area, problem or activity	
oo	**expression** a collection of terms, usually algebraic, e.g. $3x + 4 + 2x - 3$	**42**
oo	**exterior angle** the angle through which a wire is bent at each vertex, when making a polygon from a straight piece of wire	**90**

MATHSFACT

A 20p coin weighs 5g exactly. A 50p coin weighs 8g exactly. 40g in 20p coins would be worth £1.60 but 40g in 50p coins would be worth £2.50. Does this mean that a 20p coin is really worth over 30p? Unfortunately not – 20p coin metal is slightly cheaper to make than 50p metal as it contains more copper and less nickel. Worth a try though!

G/I

age code	word and meaning	page reference
O	**face** a flat surface of a solid shape, e.g. a cube has 6 faces	*30*
O	**factor** a small number which divides exactly into a bigger number, e.g. 4 is a factor of 12	6, **7**, 31, *62*, 65, *87*
O	**factor pairs** two numbers which multiply to give the required product, e.g. (3, 20) is a factor pair of 60	**81**
O	**factor rainbow** factors listed in order and joined in pairs can create a rainbow picture; if there is only one number in the middle then the original number was a square number, e.g. 16 1 2 4 8 16	**7**
OO	**factorise** rewrite a number or algebraic expression as a product of two or more factors; numbers are written as a product of primes, while expressions are written with one or more brackets $36 = 3^2 \times 2^2$ $3y^3 = 3 \times y \times y \times y$ $3a + 6 = 3(a + 2)$	**31**, **42**
O	**Fahrenheit** the temperature scale on which water freezes at 32 degrees and boils at 212 degrees	**8**, 86
O	**fair** not biased; a fair die has an equal chance of landing on any one of its six faces	
O	**false** not true; a lie; having a logical value of zero (on a spreadsheet)	
O	**fifths** the result when a whole is divided into five equal pieces	**5**
O	**fifty-fifty chance** another expression for evens or 50% probability	*23*, **26**, 66
OO	**finite** having an end eventually	
O	**flow chart** a chain of decision boxes or instruction boxes, useful for creating a logical process or organisation of ideas	**8**, 44, 82
O	**fluid ounce (fl. oz)** an imperial measure of liquid capacity	**86**
O	**fold (1)** bend something over onto itself to double the thickness or make a crease	
O	**fold (2)** suffix meaning 'many times' as in 3-fold	13
O	**foot, feet** a unit of length consisting of 12 inches (about 30.48 cm)	**17**, 86

G/I

MATHSFACT

The letter **a** does not occur in the spelling of any of the first 100 numbers.

age code	word and meaning	page reference
O	**formula** a 'recipe' for combining numbers, using words or letters (pl. **formulae**) e.g. $P = 2(l + w)$	**8**, 41, 42, 72, 73, 86, 89, 90, 91, 94
OO	**formulae** more than one formula (also known as formulas)	58, 91, 94
O	**fraction** a quantity written as a numerator over (divided by) a denominator, e.g. $\frac{2}{3}$ (proper) $\frac{3}{2}$ (improper)	**5**, *5*, 28, 32, 33, 34, 40, 42, 44, 45, 52
O	**fraction wall** a way of comparing fractions by splitting the same width into different equal quantities	**5**
OO	**fractional shape** a shape formed from a simpler shape by cutting parts away	**61**
O	**frequency** the number of times something has happened	**21, 22, 24,** 65
O	**frequency diagram** a type of bar chart in which the vertical axis is frequency, indicated by the height of the bar	22, **24,** 64
O	**frequency table / chart** a table of collected data organised into categories and giving the total (frequency) in each category	21, **24,** 64
O	**function** a rule for changing one number into another, e.g. 'multiply by 4' or 'add 1'	8
O	**function machine** a chain of one or more functions which features an input and output of numbers	8
O	**gallon** a unit of capacity consisting of 8 pints (about 4.5 litres)	**17,** 86
OO	**general term** the term in a sequence at any desired position, also known as the nth term	**72,** 75, 89
OO	**generate** produce or continue a sequence using the given rule	**46,** 47, 72, 73

G/I

MATHSFACT

The three richest people in the world together own as much as the world's 600 million poorest.

age code	word and meaning	page reference
O	**geometry** the branch of mathematics dealing with shapes	*18*
O	**good chance** having a probability above 50%	
OO	**gradient** a measurement of the steepness of a line, given by (height increase) ÷ (width increase) 1 : 2 50%	
O	**gram** one thousandth part of a kilogram	**17**, **86**
O	**graph** a pictorial representation of data	22, **25**, **43**, 63, 64, 65, 69, 74
O	**greater than (>)** having a bigger value (note carefully which way the sign goes); the biggest number goes next to the big end of the sign, e.g. $5 > 3$	**75**
O	**greater than or equal to (≥)** having a bigger value or just the same value, e.g. if $x \geq 2$ for the score on an ordinary die, then x could be 2, 3, 4, 5 or 6	
O	**greatest value** the maximum value obtained by a set of data or a line on a graph	25
O	**grid** a network of crossed lines, usually at right angles to each other	9, 25, 56
O	**grouped data** data which has been sorted into groups (classes) of equal class interval	24
O	**half** the result when a whole is divided into two equal pieces (pl. **halves**)	5
O	**halve** divide by two	
OO	**HCF** the Highest Common Factor of two or more numbers, e.g. 8 is the HCF of 16 and 24	7, **31**
O	**hectare** a unit of area equal to 10 000 square metres (think of a square 100 m on each side); approx. 2.5 acres	**86**
O	**height** the vertical distance between the top and the ground or base height base height base	
OOO	**hemisphere** half of a sphere	**77**
OOO	**hendecagon** a polygon with eleven sides	**90**
OO	**heptagon** a polygon with seven sides	**90**
O	**hexagon** a polygon with six sides	*85, 89,* **90**

G/I

MATHSFACT

It takes 8.3 minutes for sunlight to travel 93 million miles to Earth.

age code	word and meaning	page reference
O	**high** having a large value; a measurement of the height of something	
OO	**highest common factor (HCF)** the biggest number which divides exactly into two or more larger numbers	7, **31**
OO	**histogram** a type of bar chart where the area of each bar gives the frequency	
O	**horizontal** parallel to the horizon; straight across	
O	**hour** a unit of time equal to 60 minutes or one 24th of a day	
O	**hundred, hundreds** the place value position to the left of the tens column H T U · t h	**1**, 27, 37
O	**hundredth, hundredths** the place value position to the right of the tenths column H T U · t **h**	1, **3**, 28
O	**hundredweight** one twentieth of an imperial ton (112 lb)	**17**, 86
OOO	**hypotenuse** the longest side in a right-angled triangle	**76**, 94
OOO	**icosahedron** a regular solid with twenty equilateral triangle faces	*30*
O	**identical** exactly the same in all respects; congruent (shapes)	**13**
OOO	**identically equal to** another way of saying 'equivalent to' i.e. always true	
OO	**image** the result of a transformation on an object	**59**
O	**imperial** the measurement system in use before the metric system	17, **86**
O	**impossible** not possible under any circumstance; probability 0; guaranteed to fail	**26**, *45*, 66, *75*
O	**improper fraction** a fraction in which the numerator (top) is bigger than the denominator (bottom) – can be changed into a mixed number, e.g. $\frac{3}{2} \rightarrow 1\frac{1}{2}$ $\frac{15}{4} \rightarrow 3\frac{3}{4}$	**45**
OO	**in terms of** a formula in terms of t will use only the variable t combined with numbers	**72**, 73

G/I

MATHSFACT

The one millionth digit after the decimal point in Pi is 1

age code	word and meaning	page reference
O	**inch** imperial unit of length (based originally on the length of part of a Roman thumb!) ⊢ 1 inch ⊣	**17**, 86
O	**increase** make bigger	
OO	**index** the little number which indicates repeated multiplication, squares, cubes etc., e.g. 2^3	**42**, 82
OOO	**index notation** writing numbers in a form which shows the correct power of 10 each time, e.g. 3000 is 3×10^3	
OO	**indices** one index, two indices: (*see* **powers**)	
OOO	**inequality** a statement featuring 'less than' or 'greater than'	**75**
OO	**infinite** having no end, ever; you can never reach infinity	
O	**input** a number which is 'fed into' a function machine; see **function** input — ×2 > — output	**8**
O	**instruments** mathematical equipment such as compasses and ruler	
O	**integer** a whole number such as 35 or 108 or ⁻2	
OOO	**integer solution set** all the whole numbers which satisfy a pair of inequalities, e.g. $x \leqslant 2$ and $x \geqslant {}^-2$ gives the integer solution set {⁻2, ⁻1, 0, 1, 2}	**75**
OO	**intercept** 'cut across'; a useful word to describe where a straight line crosses the y-axis	**43**
OO	**interest** money paid into a savings account by a bank or building society; usually a percentage of what was there before (compound interest)	*22*
OO	**interior angle** an angle between two adjacent sides inside a polygon; in a regular polygon all the interior angles are equal	**90**
O	**interpret** give meaning to something, especially a set of results or a diagram	
OO	**intersect (1)** the point at which two lines cross	**12**

G/I

MATHSFACT
Your heart will beat about three billion times in your lifetime.

age code	word and meaning	page reference
oo	**intersect (2)** the point at which two sets overlap	70, **93**
oo	**intersection** the point at which two intersecting lines meet; this point of intersection is on both lines	**74**
o	**interval** any part of a scale, especially on a number line	15
o	**inverse** the opposite, e.g. × and ÷; + and −; square and square root	**39**, 82
o	**inverse function** the function which does the opposite of the one given, e.g. '−3' is the inverse function of '+3'	**39**
o	**inverse mapping** the reverse mapping, e.g. $x \rightarrow x - 3$ is the inverse mapping for the mapping $x \rightarrow x + 3$	
o	**investigate** find out by asking one's own questions and looking for answers	
oo	**irregular** not regular (shapes), thus having two or more different sides and angles	
oo	**isometric** a grid of equilateral triangles, used for drawing solid shapes in two dimensions	**56**
o	**isosceles** having two sides the same length to create a line of symmetry (especially isosceles triangle and isosceles trapezium)	9, 53, 57, **85**, 90
ooo	**justify** give a reason for something, e.g. algebra as a powerful way to justify a statement such as 'odd + odd = even'	
o	**key (1)** any one of the buttons on a calculator which can be pressed in the course of a calculation	**52**
o	**key (2)** an indicator to provide essential information on a graph or scale drawing, e.g. scale 1 cm: 100 m, or a colour code for a pie chart	**19**, 25
o	**kilogram** one thousand grams; the standard unit for measuring mass	**17**, 86
o	**kilometre** one thousand metres; used for measuring long distances	**17**, 86

G/I

MATHSFACT

There are 204 squares of all possible sizes on an ordinary 8 × 8 chess board. How many would there be on one 10 × 10?

age code	word and meaning	page reference
o	**kilometres per hour (km/h)** measure of speed obtained by dividing distance travelled (in km) by time taken (in hours)	**86**
o	**kite** a symmetrical quadrilateral with two adjacent pairs of equal sides *delta*	43, 57, **85**
o	**label** the description of an axis on a graph or chart, e.g. '*y*-axis' or 'frequency'	9, **22**, 25
oo	**LCM** the Lowest Common Multiple of two or more numbers, e.g. 24 is the LCM of 8 and 3	7, **31**
oo	**least significant digit** the digit in a number which has least say in the size of the number, e.g. the 7 in 246.7	**35**
o	**least value** the minimum value attained by a set of data or a line on a graph	
o	**length** the distance between the two ends	*73*
o	**less than (<)** having a smaller value; *note carefully which way the sign goes; the biggest number goes next to the big end of the sign,* e.g. $3 < 5$ If $x < 3$ then x could be ... ⁻2, ⁻1, 0, 1, 2	**75**
o	**less than or equal to (≤)** having a smaller value or just the same value If $x \leq 3$ then x could be ... ⁻2, ⁻1, 0, 1, 2 or 3	
oo	**like terms** algebraic terms with the same letter part; these can be added or subtracted, e.g. $3x^2$, x^2 and $-2x^2$ are all like terms	**42**
o	**likelihood** chance; 'the likelihood of winning the Lottery is very small'	**26**, 66
o	**likely** describing something which has a good chance of happening	**26**
ooo	**limit** the boundary beyond which the value cannot go; when you divide any number by the number just after it, you can get as close as you like to 1 but you will never quite get there; 1 is the limit	
o	**line** originally the shortest distance between two points; in general, a line has infinite length but no breadth	
o	**line graph** a graph drawn by joining up plotted points	**25**, 43, 74

G/l

MATHSFACT

Sharks kill about 60 people every year. Mosquitoes, by comparison, kill about 1.3 million.

age code	word and meaning	page reference
OO	**line of best fit** a straight line judged by eye to go through the majority of points on a scatter graph	**69**
O	**line of symmetry** one of the mirror lines on a diagram with reflection symmetry	13, **54**, 57
O	**line segment** a piece of an infinite line, with two end points	**25**
O	**line symmetry** another name for reflection or reflective symmetry	13, **54**
OO	**linear** like a straight line	48
OO	**linear equation** an equation containing only letters and numbers i.e. no squares or cubes of letters, e.g. $3x + 4 = 2x + 7$	**48**, 49, 74
OOO	**linear expression** a type of expression with no squares or higher powers, e.g. $3x + 5$	42, **72**
OO	**linear function** a function which involves only $+$, $-$, $\times$ and $\div$ on the input number, which can be represented by a straight line, e.g. $y = 3x + 5$	**43**, 74
OO	**linear relationship** a mapping which uses only linear functions	**43**
OO	**linear sequence** a sequence of numbers, which, if plotted as y co-ordinates for consecutive x values, would lie on a straight line; going up (or down) by the same amount each time, e.g. 15, 12, 9, 6, ...	43, **46**, 72
O	**litre** one thousand millilitres; used for measuring quantities of liquid	**17**, 86
OO	**long division** a pencil and paper method of dividing one number by another	
O	**long multiplication** a pencil and paper method of multiplying two numbers	28, **37**
OO	**loss** a 'negative profit', where the money received in sales is less than the value of the goods sold	
OO	**lowest common multiple (LCM)** the smallest number into which two or more smaller numbers will divide exactly, e.g. the LCM of 6 and 9 is 18	7, **31**, 45

G/l

MATHSFACT

Every 3-D solid has a number of Faces (F), Vertices (V) and Edges (E). Euclid discovered that $F + V - E = 2$

age code	word and meaning	page reference
O	**lowest terms** describes a fraction which cannot be cancelled down (simplified) any more, e.g. $\frac{1}{3}$ $\frac{3}{7}$ $\frac{10}{21}$	**28**
O	**map (1)** a scaled picture or scale diagram of an area	**19**
O	**map (2) / mapping** a procedure for changing one number (input) to another (output)	**8**, 43
O	**map (3)** the transformation of a shape mapped onto an image by means of reflection, rotation or translation	9, **13**
O	**mass** the weight of an object, measured in grams and kilograms *(see also* **weight***)*	**23**
O	**maximum value** the greatest size a number can take in the given context	25
O	**mean** the average found by adding the data and dividing the total by the number of items, e.g. the mean of 1, 2, 3 and 18 is 6	**23**
O	**measure** the value or size of something using standard units	**17**, 86, *86*
O	**median** the average found by writing data in order and finding the middle value, or the mean of the two middle values, e.g. the median of 1, 2, 3 and 14 is 2.5	**22**, 23, 24
O	**memory** the facility for storing numbers and half-way answers to assist in a calculation, when using a calculator	
OOO	**mensuration** the process of measuring and calculating measurements	*18, 59*
O	**method** a procedure, process or 'recipe' for carrying out a calculation or operation, e.g. the method for constructing triangles needs ruler, protractor and compasses	
O	**metre** the standard unit of length, equal to one hundred centimetres or one thousand millimetres	**17**, 86
OO	**metres per second (m/s)** a unit of speed in which one metre is covered every second	**86**
O	**metric** the measurement system based upon powers of 10 with the metre as the basic unit of length	17, **86**, *86*
OO	**metric / imperial approximations** rough equivalents used to convert quickly between units in the metric and imperial systems	17, **86**

G/I

MATHSFACT

A four-dimensional space creature could take a rubber band from us and return it as a loose knot, which we could not untie without cutting the rubber band open.

age code	word and meaning	page reference
OO	**midpoint** the half-way point along a line, e.g. the point of intersection of the diagonals of a parallelogram	
O	**mile** a unit of length corresponding to 'a thousand paces' (5280 feet) or about 1609 metres *(5 miles is approximately 8 km)*	**17**, 86
O	**miles per hour (mph or miles/h)** a unit of speed in which one mile is covered every hour	**86**
O	**millennium** a period of time lasting 1000 years	
O	**millilitre** one thousandth part of a litre	**17**, 86
O	**millimetre** one thousandth part of a metre	**17**, 86
O	**minimum value** the smallest size a number can take in the given context	
OOO	**minuend** the number from which another (the subtrahend) is subtracted	*36*
O	**minus (negative)** a signed or directed number which is below zero; better known as 'negative numbers'	**10**, 30
O	**minus (subtract)** take away; the second number is taken away from the first	**3**, 10
O	**minute (1) (time)** a period of time lasting 60 seconds or one 60th of an hour	
O	**minute (2)** very small	
O	**mirror line** a line through the middle of a shape where one could place a mirror and still see all of it	13, **54**, 57
O	**mixed number** a number with a whole number part and a proper fraction part; can be converted into an improper fraction for multiplying and dividing calculations e.g. $1\frac{1}{2} \rightarrow \frac{3}{2}$ $3\frac{1}{4} \rightarrow \frac{13}{4}$	**45**
OO	**mnemonic** an aid to remembering, e.g. '**N**aughty **E**lephants **S**quirt **W**ater' is a mnemonic for **N**orth **E**ast **S**outh **W**est	16, 19, *47*, 79
O	**modal class / group** the class / group in a table of grouped data which has the highest frequency	**22**, 24

G/I

MATHSFACT

At a gathering of any six people, it is always possible to find either three people who are acquaintances, or three people who have never met before.

age code	word and meaning	page reference
O	**mode** occurring most often; most frequent or most common; the average represented by the most commonly occurring data item	**22**, 24
O	**month** a period of time lasting approximately four weeks (lunar month) or 28 – 31 days (calendar month)	
OO	**most significant digit** the digit in a number which has greatest say in the size of the number, e.g. the 2 in 246.7	**50**
O	**multiple** a product, e.g. multiples of 3 are all the numbers with 3 as a factor, i.e. numbers in the 3-times table	7, *9*, 81
OOO	**multiplicand** the number which is being multiplied by something else (the multiplicator)	*36*
O	**multiplication** the process of finding the product; i.e. multiplying	1, 28, 30, **37**, *37 38*, 40, *41*, 81
OOO	**multiplicator (multiplier)** the number which is being used to multiply up another number (the multiplicand)	*36*
O	**multiply** find the product of two or more numbers; 'times', as in the times tables	*11, 21*
OO	**multiply out** multiply each term inside the brackets by the factor outside and then simplify the resultant expression	42, 94
O	**nearest** closest, especially when rounding numbers, e.g. 3467 is roughly 3470 to the nearest 10, or roughly 3500 to the nearest 100	50
O	**nearly** almost, as in 'the value of Pi is nearly 3 and one seventh'	
O	**negative** the opposite of positive; below zero, e.g. negative six is written as ⁻6	10
OO	**negative correlation** as one variable increases, the other decreases	69
O	**negative numbers** numbers which are below zero, occasionally referred to as 'minus numbers', e.g. ⁻3	**10**, *29*, 30, 83
O	**net (polyhedron)** a 'cardboard cut-out' design which can be folded up to make a solid shape	11
OO	**net (without tax)** the value or price of something before VAT has been added on	

G/I

MATHSFACT

Time slows down in space. If one twin went on a space flight he would return younger than his brother.

age code	word and meaning	page reference
O	**ninths** the result when a whole is divided into nine equal pieces	
O	**no chance** zero probability; impossible	**26**
OO	**nonagon** a polygon with nine sides	**90**
O	**north** towards the North Pole	**19**, 62, 87
O	**north-east** with north-west, south-west and south-east: the points of the compass in between the four main directions	**19**, 87
OO	**notation T(*n*)** using algebra to write down a rule or expression in a convenient form	47, **72**, **73**, 89
OO	**n^{th} term** the general term of a sequence of numbers	47, **72**, **73**, 89
O	**number line** numbers in order on a marked line, usually either side of zero (especially as an aid to mental or pencil arithmetic) for plotting points or for representing a solution set for a pair of inequalities	10, 75, **83**
O	**numerator** the top number in a fraction, e.g. $\frac{3}{4}$ $\frac{5}{3}$	40, **44**
OO	**object** the original shape before being transformed	**59**
O	**oblong** a rectangle which is not square	**57**, 85
O	**obtuse** an angle greater than 90 degrees but less than 180 degrees	**87**
O	**octagon** a polygon with eight sides	**90**
OO	**octahedron** a regular solid shape with eight equilateral triangle faces	
O	**odd** a number which ends in 1, 3, 5, 7 or 9	*2*, *84*
O	**operation** the four basic calculations done with numbers (+, −, ×, ÷)	**39**
O	**opposite (1)** facing; on the other side; in a triangle, the side furthest from the angle	79, **85**
O	**opposite (2)** an inverse, e.g. multiplication is the opposite of division	**39**

G/I

MATHSFACT

Start with any quadrilateral. Draw a square on each side, the same length as that side. When you join the centres of opposite squares, the two lines will be equal and perpendicular.

age code	word and meaning	page reference
OO	**opposite angles (1)** when two lines cross, they make an X shape: the angles above and below the point of intersection are opposite and equal angles; left and right are also opposite and equal	**53**
OO	**opposite angles (2)** two interior angles on opposite sides in a polygon; they can be joined by a diagonal which cuts the polygon in half	57, **85**
OO	**opposite sides** sides in a polygon which are separated by the width of the shape – the polygon centre lies between them; a regular polygon with an odd number of sides has no pairs of opposite sides	
O	**order (to list)** e.g. a set of numbers according to size	35, 44
O	**order (of operations)** the rules which say which of the various operations (e.g. +, −, ×, ÷) are to be given priority; also known as **BODMAS** or **BIDMAS**	8, **41**
OO	**order (of rotation symmetry)** the number of ways in which a plane shape appears the right way up (maps onto itself) while being turned through 360 degrees order 2 order 3	13, **55**
O	**origin** the point with co-ordinates (0, 0) on an (x,y) grid	**9**, 43, 69
OO	**original value** the size of something at the beginning, commonly before a percentage change	
O	**ounce** a unit of mass (abbreviated oz) which represents one sixteenth of a pound weight (about 28 g)	17, **86**
OO	**outcome** a possible result of a particular event	*63, 68*
OO	**outcome table** a systematic way of displaying all possible outcomes to an experiment	**68**
O	**output** a number which 'comes out' of a function machine	**8**

G/I

MATHSFACT

In 1792, a year after Mozart's death, a system of 'automatic music' was published consisting of charts and tables of musical sections. New music was generated by rolling two dice in order to determine which bars were to be joined together.

age code	word and meaning	page reference
OOO	**P(*n*) for probability of event *n*** p(heads) is shorthand for 'the probability of getting heads'	
O	**parallel** running in the same direction	11, *48*, **53**, 56, **57** 85
O	**parallelogram** a quadrilateral with two pairs of parallel sides	43, 54, **57**, **85**, 91
O	**partition** separating a number into its parts, e.g. 126 = 100 + 20 + 6 (the hundreds, tens and units parts)	
O	**pattern (1)** an arrangement of objects, e.g. matches, counters or tiles, according to some rule which enables a sequence to be made	**6**
O	**pattern (2)** a pattern of numbers enabling us to predict the next number in the sequence	**46**, 47, 72
O	**pattern (3)** a geometrical design which is built up by applying rules of symmetry	
O	**pentagon** a polygon with five sides regular pentagon	*30*, *65*, *89*, **90**
OO	**per** divided by; for each one; out of; as in **per**cent or metres **per** second	*33*
O	**percentage (%)** a number which is a fraction of 100, e.g. 30% = 30/100	**5**, 32, 33, *33*, 44, 52, 65
O	**perimeter** the distance all the way around the edge of a shape	**18**
O	**perpendicular** at right angles	
OO	**perpendicular bisector** a line which cuts another line in half, meeting it at right angles; the construction using ruler and compasses which creates this line	
OO	**pi (π)** the ratio of a circle's circumference to its diameter, approximately 3.14	58, *58*, **91**, **92**, *92*

G/I

MATHSFACT

It is possible to construct an overhanging stack of books so that the top book lies completely beyond the bottom book.

age code	word and meaning	page reference
O	**pictogram** a diagram similar to a bar chart in which appropriate pictures are put in lines to make the (usually) horizontal bars happy ☺☺☺☺ unhappy ☹☹ ☺ represents 2 children	
OO	**pie chart** a circular diagram in which the size of each sector shows the proportion of the whole (60° 210°)	63, **65**
O	**pint** a unit of capacity (usually liquid) consisting of 20 fluid ounces (about 0.6 litres)	**17**, 86
O	**place value** units, Tens, Hundreds etc.; the size of a number depends on its position H T U·t h	**1**, 27, *27*, 35
O	**plan** a bird's eye view of a solid, especially used to show floor layouts in buildings	
O	**plan view** the view from above	
O	**plane** a flat surface; 2-dimensional, like a sheet of paper	
O	**plane shapes** two-dimensional shapes which are drawn on paper, as opposed to solid shapes, which can be picked up	53, 54, 55, **57**, 58, 59, 60, 85, 90, 91
OOO	**plane symmetry** the three dimensional equivalent in solids of line symmetry in plane shapes	
O	**plot** mark a small cross to indicate a position of a point	**9**
O	**plus** the arithmetical sign (+) to indicate addition	
O	**pm (p.m.)** (Latin) *post meridiem* means 'after noon'; (*see also* **am (a.m.)**)	**83**
O	**point** a position often indicated by a cross; having no dimension	
OO	**polygon** a shape with straight sides	53, **90**, *90*
O	**poor chance** having a probability below 50%	
O	**position** another name for place or location; in mathematics we describe positions precisely using co-ordinates	**9**
O	**positive** above zero on the number line, e.g. positive three is written as +3 or simply 3	9, **10**

G/I

MATHSFACT

Three identical glasses can be stacked base on rim, if the two upper glasses are in the '10:00' and '2:00' positions relative to the bottom glass 'clockface' viewed from above.

age code	word and meaning	page reference
OO	**positive correlation** as one variable increases, so too does the other	69
O	**possibility** one of the things which could happen	66
OO	**possibility space** a table listing systematically all possible outcomes of an experiment	68
O	**possible** having a probability which is greater than 0	66
O	**pound (money) (£1)** equal to 100 pence	25
O	**pound (weight) (1 lb)** equal to 16 oz (about 0.5 kg)	17, 86
OO	**power** the top right (index) number used in squares, cubes etc. to indicate repeated multiplying, e.g. 2^3 means 2 to the power of 3 (i.e. $2 \times 2 \times 2$)	*16*, **31**, 42, 82
OO	**predict** guess the outcome of a future event, usually choosing the outcome with the highest probability	6
O	**prime** a number which has only two factors, 1 and itself	2, 7, *7*, 31, 70, *81*, 81
OO	**prime factor** a factor which is prime; a number which divides exactly into a larger number but which does not itself have any smaller factors besides itself and 1, e.g. the prime factors of 14 are 2 and 7	31
OO	**prime factor decomposition** writing a composite number as a product of its prime factors, e.g. $180 = 2 \times 2 \times 3 \times 3 \times 5$	31
OO	**prism** a solid which has the same shaped cross-section all the way through	**56**, 91
O	**probability** the branch of mathematics which looks at the chance of things happening	*19*, *23*, **26**, *63*, 66, *66*, 67
O	**probability scale** the number line from 0 (impossible) to 1 (certain) 0 ⊢———————————————⊣ 1 impossible unlikely even chance likely certain	26, **66**
OO	**probability sum** it is always certain that something will happen, so the sum of all probabilities at any time is 1	67
OOO	**probability tree** the branching diagram used to keep track of multiple-event probabilities	

G/I

age code	word and meaning	page reference
O	**probable** another name for possible, but usually used to mean with a probability greater than 50%	**26**
O	**procedure** a sequence of instructions	**37**
O	**problem** any kind of question to which an answer is needed	
O	**product** the result of a multiplication	**31**, *36*, 42, 81
OO	**product of prime factors** a way of writing any whole number as a product of its component primes, e.g. 60 = 2 × 2 × 3 × 5	**31**
OO	**profit** the overall gain made by the seller when something is sold; profit = selling price – cost price	
OOO	**proof** a logically strong argument which explains why something is always true *(note that an example does not make a proof!)*	
O	**proper fraction** a fraction in which the numerator (top) is smaller than the denominator (bottom) – when written in decimal form it will be between 0 and 1 e.g. $\frac{3}{4}$ = 0.75	**5**, 45
O	**property** a characteristic of something, e.g. one of the properties of a kite is that it has one line of symmetry	54, **57**, 85, 90
O	**proportion** any of several ways (e.g. fraction or percentage) used to describe part of a whole, e.g. 'the proportion of girls in this room is about three fifths'	**32**
OOO	**proportional to (in proportion to)** where one number multiplied by another number requires the second to be multiplied by the same number, e.g. adapting a recipe for a different number of people	**34**, 59
OOO	**proportionality** the property of being in proportion	
O	**protractor** geometrical instrument used to measure angles, commonly made of a semicircle of clear plastic	
OOO	**prove** provide an argument which leaves no room for doubt	
OOO	**pyramid** a solid with a flat (esp. square) base and the other faces sloping up to a point at the apex	11, *14*, 77, *77*, *89*, **91**

G/I

MATHSFACT

In the Egyptian Rhind Papyrus (c. 1650 B.C.) the symbol for 'plus' is denoted by a pair of legs walking towards the number to be added.

age code	word and meaning	page reference
OOO	**Pythagoras** the mathematician whose theorem calculates sides of right-angled triangles	**76**, *76*, 94, *94*
OOO	**Pythagorean triple** any set of three integers which could be lengths in a right-angled triangle, e.g. (3, 4, 5) or (5, 12, 13) $3^2 + 4^2 = 5^2$	**94**
OO	**quadrant** one of the four areas separated by the x,y axes; quarter of a circle; (the 'First Quadrant' is the one where x and y are both positive, and they are then counted anticlockwise)	**43**
OOO	**quadratic** a type of equation or expression which has an x-squared term, but not higher $x^2 + 3x$ (expression); $x^2 + 3x - 2 = 0$ (equation)	**71**, *73*
OOO	**quadratic function** a function which includes squaring as well as the other arithmetical functions	**71**
OOO	**quadratic sequence** a sequence of numbers, which, if plotted one after the other, would lie on a curve such as $y = x^2$	71, **73**
O	**quadrilateral** a polygon with four sides	57, *57*, **85**, 90
O	**quarters** the result of a whole divided into four equal pieces	**5**, *12*
O	**questionnaire** a carefully planned set of unbiased questions used to collect information from people in a survey	
OO	**quotient** the (whole number) answer to a division; a ratio or fraction which gives this answer *(see also **remainder**)*, e.g. 13 ÷ 5 → **2** remainder 3	**36**
OO	**radius** the distance from the centre of a circle to the circumference (pl. radii)	12, 58, **92**

G/I

MATHSFACT

One drop of human saliva from a healthy person contains about 150 000 000 bacteria.

age code	word and meaning	page reference
OO	**random** occurring by chance alone; unpredictable; any one of several possibilities	**66**
O	**range** the difference between the greatest and least values in a set of data	**22**, 23, 24
OOO	**range of values** when grouping data, each category is a suitable range of values, the same width as all the others	**24**
OOO	**rate (1)** the measure of progress or increase with time, metres per second; litres per hour etc.	**78**
O	**rate (2)** the amount of one currency given in exchange for another ('exchange rate')	**25**
OO	**ratio** a way of comparing the relative size of two or more whole numbers, e.g. 3 : 2	**34**
OO	**raw data** data as gathered in a survey, before being 'processed' by grouping, averages, graphs etc.	24
O	**reason** an explanation given in answer to the question 'why?'	
O	**reasoning** the process of clear thinking which uses logic and careful explanation	
OO	**record (noun and verb)** information gathered in a survey and written down carefully in a table; an entry in a database	
O	**rectangle** a quadrilateral with four right angles (see also **oblong**)	57, **85**, 91
OOO	**recurring decimal** a fraction converted into decimal form which continues in a repeated pattern for ever, e.g. 2/9 = 0.222…	51
OO	**reduce / reduction** the opposite of increase / enlargement	**32**
O	**reflect** draw the result of a reflection in a given mirror line	**13**, 17, 54
O	**reflection (1)** the image seen in a mirror or mirror line	**13**, 17, 54
O	**reflection (2)** the transformation which maps an object into its reflected image	**13**, 17, 54

G/I

MATHSFACT

Talking to your friend on Jupiter would require patience. There would be an 80 minute pause between your question and their reply as the radio signal went there and back.

age code	word and meaning	page reference
O	**reflection symmetry** the property of having matching halves either side of one or more mirror lines	**13**, *17*, 54, *54*, 57
O	**reflex** describes an angle which is bigger than 180 degrees	**87**
OO	**region (1)** a part of a surface, e.g. one marked out by lines on a grid or in a shape	**61**, 92
OO	**region (2)** part of a Venn diagram which illustrates a subset of the universal data set	**93**
OO	**regular** having all the sides the same length and all the angles equal (regular polygons)	*30*, 53, **90**, *90*
OO	**relationship** the connection between two or more numbers, including unknown numbers, often written as a formula	8
OO	**remainder** division gives a whole number part (quotient) and a remainder, either of which can be zero, e.g. 13 ÷ 5 → 2 remainder **3**	4
OO	**represent** give in another form, especially as a diagram or graph	
O	**result (1)** the outcome of a survey or experiment, best displayed in a table	**22**, 65
O	**result (2)** the final answer to a numerical problem or calculation	
O	**result (3)** the effect of completing a transformation such as rotation or reflection	
O	**rhombus (diamond)** a symmetrical quadrilateral which has four equal sides	43, 57, **85**
O	**right (1)** correct	*see own ex. book*
O	**right (2)** describes an angle size of 90°	53, 57, 85, **87**
O	**right-angled** with one or more angles of 90 degrees	57, **85**
OO	**risk** a gamble; an experiment where failure has a non-zero probability	

G/I

MATHSFACT

If you laid 109 pennies in a straight line you would get an idea of the width of the Sun. Each penny represents the Earth.

age code	word and meaning	page reference
O	**rotate** draw the result of a rotation through a given angle and about a given point	**13**
O	**rotation (1)** turning around a fixed point	**13**, *17*
	rotation (2) the transformation which maps an object onto its rotated image	**13**, *17*
O	**rotation symmetry** the property of having two or more 'right ways up'	**13**, 53, 55, 57
O	**rough** approximate	
O	**roughly** not given to a high degree of accuracy, e.g. an approximation	
OO	**round (1)** simplify or approximate an answer so that fewer figures are required to write it down	35, 50, **51**
O	**round (2)** the shape of a circle	
O	**row** the horizontal in a table (left – right)	
O	**rule (1)** the instructions for generating a sequence of numbers	**47**, 71, 72, 73
	rule (2) a straight line, as drawn by pencil and ruler	
O	**ruler** any instrument for drawing straight lines or measuring length	
OO	**sale price** the new price of an item after a reduction or discount has been applied	
OO	**sample** a selection, preferably random and unbiased, for the purpose of a survey or experiment	
OOO	**sample space** an organised list of all the possible samples that could be made, also called an 'outcome' space	**68**
OO	**satisfies** a value satisfies an equation if the equation can be shown to be true when the value is substituted in	**48**, 74, 75
O	**scale (1)** measuring scales such as rulers, bathroom scales, electricity meters etc.	**15**, *15*, 87
OO	**scale (2)** a unitary ratio, e.g. 1: 20 000 which means that 1 cm on the drawing represents 20 000 cm (200 m) in real life	19, **62**

G/I

MATHSFACT

5 million tonnes of mass are burned up in the Sun's nuclear reactor every second.

age code	word and meaning	page reference
OO	**scale (3)** used when drawing a graph to choose the right scale on the axes so that all the numbers can be plotted on the paper clearly	**25**
OO	**scale drawing** a drawing accurately drawn from scaled measurements from the original	12, **62**, 87
OO	**scale factor** used to reduce or enlarge the original, e.g. on a diagram or map	**59**, 60, *60*
O	**scalene** all sides of different length, e.g. scalene triangle	**85**
OO	**scatter graph** points of paired data (e.g. height, weight) plotted as (*x,y*) co-ordinates in order to test whether or not there is a relationship (correlation) between the two	**69**
O	**sea level** a zero reference height defined by the average of high and low tides, so that all other heights can be compared with it (above and below)	**10**
O	**second (1)** the one after the first and before the third	
O	**second (2)** a unit of time equal to one sixtieth of a minute	
OO	**section** a piece, especially when referring to a part of a line or part of a shape; also used to mean 'cross-section'	
OO	**sector** part of a circle cut out by two radii, e.g. 'a pie slice' in a pie chart	65, 77, **92**
OO	**segment** part of a circle cut out by a chord	**92**
OO	**semicircle** half of a circle, cut out by a diameter	61, **92**
O	**sequence** a list of numbers following a logical pattern or rule, e.g. 1, 3, 5, 7, 9, …	6, **46**, 47, 72, 73
OO	**service charge** the extra charge on a bill to pay for services, e.g. in a restaurant, the charge for the waiter or waitress	

G/I

MATHSFACT

A male rhino beetle can support 850 times its own weight on its back. This is equivalent to an adult human lifting 76 family cars at once.

age code	word and meaning	page reference
OO	**set** a collection of things which all have something in common, e.g. {children who learn the piano}, {prime numbers}, {quadrilaterals} etc.	**70**, 93
OO	**set notation** the collection of symbols used to describe things in sets	**93**
OO	**set square** triangular device used to draw/measure angles of (45, 45, 90) degrees or (30, 60, 90) degrees	
O	**sevenths** the result of a whole divided into seven equal pieces	
O	**shape** a geometrical figure; an enclosed space or form	
O	**share** divide a given amount equally	
O	**side (1)** a straight line between the vertices in a geometric shape	**18**
OO	**side (2)** reference to either left or right of the = sign in an equation	48
O	**sign** the direction of a number, shown as $^+$ (which is often omitted) or $^-$ in front of the number	10
O	**sign change key** the key [+/−] or [(−)] on a calculator which changes the sign of a directed number	
OO	**significant figures** a form of rounding which is concerned more with the order of magnitude of the number than with the number of decimal places	**50**
OO	**similar** having the same shape, but of a different size, e.g. an enlargement	13, **59**, 60
OO	**similarity** the property of being similar, i.e. the same shape (not to be confused with its non-mathematical meaning of 'being nearly the same')	
OO	**simplest form (lowest terms)** most commonly used to refer to fractions after they have been cancelled by removing common factors above and below; also used for ratios, e.g. $\frac{3}{6} \to \frac{1}{2}$ $9:12 \to \mathbf{3:4}$	**28**
OO	**simplify** reduce to a simpler form, especially with fractions, ratios and algebraic expressions, e.g. $\frac{2}{6} \to \frac{1}{3}$; $4:2 \to 2:1$; $3x + 4x \to 7x$	28, **32**, 42, 45, 51

G/I

MATHSFACT

The Lockheed SR.71A aircraft can travel at 3530 km per hour. This is faster than a bullet shot from a rifle.

age code	word and meaning	page reference
OOO	**simultaneous equations** two or more equations which need to be solved at the same time, e.g. $x + y = 10$ $x - y = 4$	**74**
OOO	**sine (sin)** in a right-angled triangle, the sine of an angle is equal to the ratio opposite : hypotenuse or opposite ÷ hypotenuse	79
O	**sixths** the result when a whole is divided into six equal pieces	**5**
O	**sketch** a diagram drawn more for convenience than accuracy	
OO	**slope** gradient; sloping	
O	**solid** a three-dimensional shape which can be picked up and handled, as opposed to plane shapes which can only be seen on paper e.g.	**71, 75**
OO	**solution** the answer to a problem, equation or inequality	**48**, 49
OO	**solve** find the value of the variable, by a systematic method, which will make the equation correct	**48**, 49, 71
O	**south** towards the South Pole	19, 87
OOO	**speed** the rate at which distance is travelled, commonly in metres per second or miles per hour	44, **78**, *78*
OOO	**sphere** a ball-shaped solid	77
OO	**spin** turn (usually fast) especially to determine an outcome, e.g. coin, spinner etc.	
OO	**spinner** anything capable of spinning, especially one which can indicate a variety of possible outcomes	
O	**square (1)** a regular quadrilateral	*4, 57, 63, 73,* **85,** 91

G/I

MATHSFACT

If you lined up 1000 pollen grains in a row, you could still hide them behind a grain of sand.

age code	word and meaning	page reference
O	**square (2)** to multiply a number by itself; the result obtained when this is done, e.g. 3 × 3 = 9	*7, 49, 60, 73, 82, 82, 94*
O	**square centimetre** a square, one centimetre on each side; a unit of area for small shapes and regions, such as those drawn in exercise books	17, **18**, 86
O	**square inch** a square, one inch on each side; an imperial unit for area occasionally seen in the measurement of pressures (e.g. pounds per square inch or p.s.i. as on some car tyres)	**86**
O	**square kilometre** a square, one kilometre on each side; a unit of area for very large shapes and regions, such as countries	**18**, 86
O	**square metre** a square, one metre on each side; a unit of area for large shapes and regions, such as playgrounds and tennis courts	17, **18**, 86
O	**square mile** a square, one mile on each side	
O	**square millimetre** a square, one millimetre on each side; a unit of area for very small shapes and regions, such as things seen under a microscope	**18**
O	**square number** the result of multiplying a whole number by itself; can be drawn as a square of dots, e.g. 1, 4, 9, 16, 25 etc.	4, 7, 31, 73, **82**, 89
O	**square root** the number which when squared gives the one at the start, e.g. the square root of 64 is 8	**82**
O	**square yard** a square, one yard on each side	17, 86
O	**square-based pyramid** a solid shape with a square base, with the other four faces rising to a single point – the shape of the famous pyramids in Egypt	**11**
OO	**squared** multiplied by itself, as in three squared is nine (written as $3^2 = 9$)	*49, 60, 94*

G/I

MATHSFACT

The longest domino topple in the world contained 4 079 381 dominoes (Leeuwarden, 2006).

age code	word and meaning	page reference
OOO	**standard (index) form** *(see **index notation**)*	
O	**statistics** the branch of mathematics dealing with understanding data	**21, 22,** 23, **24, 25,** *62,* 63, 64, 65, 69
OO	**steepness** a measure of the slope or gradient of a line; *(very steep lines are almost vertical)*	
O	**stone** a unit of weight equivalent, in Earth's gravity, to a mass of 14 pounds (6.35 kg)	**17,** 86
O	**straight angle** two lines which meet at an angle of 180°, thus making a single straight line	**87**
OO	**straight edge** any kind of ruler or similar which is used only to assist with drawing diagrams and constructions	
OO	**straight line graph** a graph of a linear function, such as $y = 5x + 2$	43, 74
OO	**subset** a set of related objects which forms part of a larger set , for example {girls in Year 7} is a subset of the set {girls in the school}	70, **93**
OO	**substitute** replace the letters in an algebraic expression with numerical values	**41,** 73, 74
	substitution the process of changing letters into numbers in order to evaluate an expression	**41,** 73, 74
O	**subtract** minus, take away; the second number is the one being taken away	**3,** 10, 41, 45
O	**subtraction** the process of taking away one number from another	**3**
OOO	**subtrahend** the number which is being subtracted from the larger number (minuend), e.g. 24 − **15** = 9	*36*
O	**sum** the answer to an addition	9, *36*
OOO	**summand** one of the numbers being added together to make the sum	*36*
OO	**supplementary angles** two angles which add up to 180 degrees $a + b = 180°$	53
O	**surface** the outside of a solid shape	
OO	**surface area** the total area of each surface of a solid shape	18

G/

MATHSFACT

Temperatures in Verkhoyansk, Russia, have spanned 105 °C, from ⁻68 °C to 37 °C.

age code	word and meaning	page reference
O	**survey** a data collection exercise which usually involves a questionnaire of some kind	**21**, 65
OO	**symbol** any sign used in mathematics to give a particular meaning, such as the symbol used for Pi (π) or 'less than' (<)	42, 58, 93
O	**symmetrical** having symmetry of any kind	**13**
O	**symmetry** sameness, especially with reflection or rotation	**13**, 54, 55
O	**symmetry lines** mirror lines on a diagram which has reflection symmetry	13, **54**
OO	**systematic** having an organised approach, especially with regard to the creation of lists	**68**, *68*
O	**table** any two-way chart which helps to organise the information it contains	21, 24
O	**tables** multiplication tables from 1 × 1 to 12 × 12	7, **81**
O	**tally** counting via the 'five bar gate' method or using ticks, which are later totalled to give the frequency IIII 4 ┼┼┼┼ 5 ┼┼┼┼I 6	**21**, 24
O	**tally chart** a diagram used to collect data by making marks in the appropriate row or column	**21**, 24
OOO	**tangent (1)** any straight line which just touches the circumference of a circle; it touches in one place and is always at right angles to the radius at that point	**92**
OOO	**tangent (2) (tan)** in a right-angled triangle, the tangent of an angle is equal to the ratio opposite : adjacent or opposite ÷ adjacent opposite hypotenuse adjacent	79
OO	**tax** any form of duty added on to the price of something	
O	**temperature** measured by a thermometer, usually in degrees Celsius	8, **10**, 86
O	**ten, tens** the place value position to the left of the Units column H **T** U·t h	**1**, *1*, 27, 37

G/I

MATHSFACT

The prolific output of Swiss mathematician Leonhard Euler (1707–83) was such that his papers were still being published for the first time more than 50 years after his death.

age code	word and meaning	page reference
o	**tenth, tenths (1)** the place value position to the right of the decimal point H T U · **t** h	**3**, 27, 28, *28*, 35
o	**tenths (2)** the result when a whole is divided into ten equal pieces	**5**
oo	**term (1)** a sequence made up of a list numbers generated by a rule; each number in the list is called a term	**46**, 47, 72, 73
oo	**term (2)** a component of an algebraic expression, separated by + or − signs, e.g. 'like terms' or 'x^2 terms'	**42**, 48
oo	**terminating decimal** a fraction converted into decimal form which terminates (stops), e.g. $\frac{3}{4} = 0.75$	
oo	**tessellate** fit together on a flat surface so that no gaps are left; rectangles tessellate but circles do not	*45, 57*
oo	**tessellation** shapes fitted together to cover a plane without gaps	*45*
oo	**tetrahedron** a regular triangular-based pyramid	
oo	**theoretical probability** assuming all outcomes are equally likely, the theoretical probability is (the number of ways of getting what you want) ÷ (the total number of equally likely outcomes)	**66**
ooo	**theory** any idea which has support or evidence, but needs proof before it is accepted as true fact	
oo	**therefore** as a result, following on from which, my conclusion is etc.	
o	**thermometer** an instrument used to measure temperature	10
o	**thickness** the measurement of height for solid objects which are almost flat	
o	**thirds** the result when a whole is divided into three equal pieces	**5**, *12*
o	**thousand, thousands** the place value position to the left of the Hundreds column **Th** H T U · t h th	

MATHSFACT

M Hari Prasad of Bangalore correctly calculated the square root of a six-digit number (732 915) without the use of a calculator or computer in 1 minute 3.8 seconds at the Indian Institute of Science on October 30, 1999.

age code	word and meaning	page reference
O	**thousandth, thousandths** the place value position to the right of the Hundredths column Th H T U · t h **th**	
O	**three-dimensional (3-D)** solid, such that it may be picked up or viewed from different positions	**11**, 56
OO	**three-figure bearing** a direction given as degrees clockwise from north	**62**
OO	**through 90°** etc. a rotation needs a rotation centre to determine the point of turning, and an angle of rotation, e.g. 'through 180 degrees' to say through how much the object is to be turned	**55**
O	**time** any interval along the line from past, through present, to future, or any fixed position on that line	*69*, **78**, *83*
OO	**time graph (line graph)** any type of graph which shows the way something is changing over time, e.g. a temperature graph, a travel graph, a happiness graph	**25**
O	**times** (as in 'three times four') *(see* **multiply***)*	
O	**timetable** a schedule of times, usually of events through the day or week, e.g. bus, train, and school lessons	
O	**title** a descriptive heading, especially important at the top of any graph, diagram or new piece of work	
OO	**to one decimal place (to 1 d.p.)** a form of rounding which is accurate to the nearest tenth U . t h → U . t h 0 . 3 6 0 . 4 to 1 d.p.	**28**
OO	**to the power of** *n* repeatedly multiplied by itself *n* times (*n* = 2 for squaring and *n* = 3 for cubing)	*16*
O	**ton** an imperial unit for weighing very heavy objects; one ton is 160 stone (about twelve men) which is 2240 lb	**17**, 86
O	**tonne** one thousand kilograms, used for measuring the mass of very heavy objects; a metric tonne is only slightly lighter than an imperial ton	**17**, 86

G/I

MATHSFACT

One of the most important early Maths books to come out of Spain was Juan Perez de Moya's *Arithmetica*, published in 1592.

age code	word and meaning	page reference
O	**total** the result of adding *(see also* **sum***)*	**21**, *34*
OO	**transform** change, especially by means of a rotation, translation, reflection or enlargement	9, **20**, 54, 55, 57
OO	**transformation** a change, especially on a shape, for example reflection, rotation, enlargement	**20**, **54**, 55, 57
O	**translate** a slide – the transformation which has no effect except a change of position	**9, 20**
O	**translation** the transformation by which a shape is translated	**9, 20**
O	**trapezium** a quadrilateral with one pair of parallel sides	9, 43, 57, **85**, 91
OO	**trial and improvement** a method for solving equations by improving on each earlier trial	**71**
O	**triangle** a plane shape with 3 sides	12, 53, **85**, **90**, **91**
OO	**triangular number** one of the numbers which can be drawn as an equilateral triangle of dots; a number in the sequence 1, 3, 6, 10, 15, … the nth triangular number is given by $\frac{1}{2}n(n+1)$	**89**
OO	**triangular prism** a solid shape with a continuous triangular cross-section which remains congruent between the two ends	
O	**true** not false; correct, straight, honest	
O	**two-dimensional (2-D)** flat, such that it can not be picked up; like a shadow or picture	**56**
OO	**two-way table** used for sorting into rows and columns, e.g. a bus timetable, football results sheet	
O	**uncertain** having a probability which is less than one, and commonly used to mean with a probability less than 0.5	26
O	**unfair** biased; not favouring both sides equally	26
OO	**unit fraction** any fraction with a numerator of one, e.g. $\frac{1}{2}$, $\frac{1}{3}$, $\frac{1}{5}$, $\frac{1}{23}$	

G/I

MATHSFACT

The standard method of long division was first seen in print in 1491, in a book by Filippo Calandri of Florence.

age code	word and meaning	page reference
OO	**unitary method** calculating with ratios in which you find out the value of one item before multiplying by the number required	**34**
O	**units (1)** the place value position to the left of the decimal point H T **U** · t h	**1**, 3, 37
O	**units (2)** the quantity being measured, e.g. cm, kg, min	**17**, 18, 86
OO	**universal set** the greatest set of all; contains everything in the question ('the universe')	70, **93**
OO	**unknown** anything not known, especially the variable letter in an equation	8, 48
O	**unlikely** having a low chance or likelihood	**26**
OO	**value** the arithmetical result of substituting given values into an algebraic expression and evaluating the expression which remains	**41**
OO	**value added tax (VAT)** a legally-required tax added on to the price of certain things	
OO	**variable** the letter in an equation representing the value to be found; the letters used in a formula or algebraic expression	48
OO	**Venn diagram** a diagram using overlapping circles to show how two or more sets are related	**70**, *70*, 93, *93*
OO	**verify** check that something is true	
OO	**vertex** a corner of a shape (pl. **vertices**)	**90**
O	**vertical** perpendicular to the horizontal; straight up	
OO	**vertically opposite angles** in an X formed by two lines crossing, angles facing each other rather than side by side are 'vertically opposite'	53
OO	**vertices** (sing. **vertex**); corners of a plane or solid shape	**90**
OO	**view** the picture you get of a three-dimensional shape when seen from the side (elevation view) or the top (plan view)	109
O	**volume** the amount of space inside a solid shape, measured in cubic cm (cm³), cubic m (m³), etc.	*16*, **18**, *60*, 77, *77*, 91

G/I

age code	word and meaning	page reference
oo	**volume factor** the old volume was multiplied by this to obtain the new volume; the volume factor is the cube of the scale factor	**60**
o	**vulgar fractions** an ordinary fraction with the numerator smaller than the denominator, e.g. $\frac{3}{5}$	**45**
o	**week** a period of time lasting seven days	
o	**weight** the force due to gravity exerted by something with mass; if there is no gravity, the mass stays the same but the weight becomes zero	
o	**west** towards the setting Sun	**19**
o	**width** a measure of how wide something is	
o	**word formula** a set of instructions or a flow diagram, which tells you what to do with the input	**8**
o	*x*-**axis** the horizontal axis on a co-ordinate grid	**9**, 43
o	*x*-**co-ordinate** the first number of a co-ordinate pair, to indicate the distance to the right (negative means to the left) e.g. (**3**,2)	**9**, 43
o	**yard** a unit of length consisting of three feet or 36 inches (about 91.4 cm)	**17**, 86
o	*y*-**axis** the vertical axis on a co-ordinate grid	**9**, 43
o	*y*-**co-ordinate** the second number of a co-ordinate pair, to indicate the distance above the *x*-axis (negative means below the *x*-axis), e.g. (3,**2**)	**9**, 43
o	**year** a period of time lasting twelve months; the time taken for Earth to travel once round the Sun	
o	**zero (1) (place holder)** nought; nothing, e.g. the zero in 3028 means 'no hundreds'	**1**, 3, 27, *27*

G/I

MATHSFACT

The distance to the edge of the observable universe is estimated to be about 78 billion light years. This distance is so great that when astronomers watch distant stars exploding, they are actually watching an event which occurred billions of years ago, since the light of the explosion has taken that long to reach the telescope.

age code	word and meaning	page reference
o	**zero (2)** the reference point on a measuring scale; when measuring a length or an angle, make sure you line up with zero on the ruler / protractor and not the edge of the plastic. 0 1 2 3 0°————180°	 10, 30, 75

G/I

MATHSFACT

Had it not been for the Great Fire of London (1666), Sir Christopher Wren would have been more famous as a mathematician than as an architect. He was Professor of Astronomy from 1657 until 1673.

MATHSFACT

Evariste Galois, a French mathematician famous for his algebra, lived only until he was 20 years old. He was shot in a duel in 1832.

MATHSFACT

The first maths textbook printed in England was by Yorkshireman Cuthbert Tonstall in 1522. Being page after page of arithmetic, in Latin, it did not sell very well! Tonstall went on to become Bishop of Durham.

MATHSFACT

The most common number to feature in British pub names is three.

G/I

MATHSFACT

(Hanson's Theorem) Take any prime number except 3 and square it. Now add the digits of your answer together. Keep adding the digits in your answer until you get left with just a single digit. You will only ever get the result 1, 4 or 7